THE
DONKEY
WHO
ALWAYS
COMPLAINED

A Parable for Moderns

The DONKEY WHO ALWAYS COMPLAINED

BY FRANCIS BEAUCHESNE THORNTON

ILLUSTRATIONS BY JOHANNES TROYER

P. J. KENEDY & SONS · NEW YORK

To

MARGARET JUDGE

With Affection

THE DONKEY

When fishes flew and forests walked
    And figs grew upon thorn,
Some moment when the moon was blood
    Then surely I was born.

With monstrous head and sickening cry
    And ears like errant wings,
The devil's walking parody
    On all four-footed things.

The tattered outlaw of the earth,
    Of ancient crooked will;
Starve, scourge, deride me: I am dumb,
    I keep my secret still.

Fools! For I also had my hour;
    One far fierce hour and sweet:
There was a shout about my ears,
    And palms before my feet.

GILBERT KEITH CHESTERTON

THE
DONKEY
WHO
ALWAYS
COMPLAINED

ONE

Long ago, in Jerusalem, lived a little donkey named
Balo. Her coat was like silver when you breathe on it.
Long ears topped her head. One of them bent down
as if it were continually bowing to the other donkeys.
Balo's two mournful eyes looked out on the great
world. On each of her sides was a smooth spot worn
by the red water jars she carried up and down the
hills and narrow streets. Her hoofs were four pieces
of yellow amber scarred by the cobblestones. Six
brass bells on her collar went "tinkle, tinkle," at
every step. By her side trotted a little silver colt that
seemed to be all legs and nose.

All day long up and down the streets went Balo
and her colt, trot, trot, jog, jog. "Tinkle, tinkle," said
the collar bells. "Wateer, wateer," sang Balo's master,
the Gypsy. Under the red turban his forehead wrinkled; his lips were puffed out like two pomegranates.
"Wateer, wateer," sang back the echoes from the
overhanging balconies and the time-scarred walls.
Twinkling flowers with their pink and yellow stars in
the crannies of the piled stones seemed to dance at
the sound of the call. They remembered the dew that

fell on Mount Hermon. They heard the voice of the river Jordan calling through the nights of winter rain. Springs of living water welling in the cool yellow of the limestone caverns. Welling up with life for all the fields and flowers of the world!

"Wateer, wateer," sang the Gypsy in the red turban. Sometimes a servant maid beckoned from a half-opened door. An arm was raised with a jingle of silver bracelets. Then Balo stopped for a moment. The spigot at the bottom of the jars turned. She felt the burden on her sides lighten a little. The colt nuzzled her flank.

Sometimes a Roman halted them with a disdainful call, "Ho there, Barbarian!" Then the silver cup was taken from the fine silk wrapper. It glittered in the sun. The water in it was filled with tiny, skipping rainbows. Balo heard the clank of the bronze coin thrown against the jar. She saw the flash of her master's white teeth and watched the light glancing from a sword hilt with a vulture's head carved on it.

"Wateer, wateer!" Jog, jog, up and down the streets. The bazaars were full of shouting men. Rugs like the sunset hung there. Drifts of gold and scarlet flowers gave out an odor of joy. Yet it was not strong enough to drown the reek from the onion and garlic sellers, or the fetid smells from the stalls of fresh-slain goat's flesh that looked like mottled onyx.

In the spring the day was not too bad. There was a kind of music in the air. It sang in the flowering trees slanted above the walls, it glittered in the eyes of the children.

But in winter it was different. Balo's eyes grew mournful, like black wells under the moon. The jars chafed her sides. The wind was filled with ice-arrows. Then her heart flew back to Nazareth where she had been born and first brought up.

In summer the weather was even worse in Jerusalem. The sun seemed to be in the middle of Balo's back. Breath came short; the collar bells had a tired dusky tinkle; breathing was difficult. The colt cried and complained. A wheeze seemed ever in Balo's throat. Up and down the rough streets. The day was endless. Balo could not wait for the sun to nest in the gold temple on Mount Moriah. She was sure it rested there in the middle of the flashing pinnacles, above row on row of gigantic pillars. Then as light ran up the sky her master took her down to the corral of the donkeys beyond the Roman temple in the valley. Sparse grass grew there. Sometimes there was a pile or two of mouldy hay. But there were many donkeys —tired, dirty, and hungry—always hungry. Food was never enough. Balo remembered the evening a young girl tossed her a sheaf of meadow grass; it smelled of wood violets and thyme. It made her heart yearn for the hills near Nazareth, after the rains were over. She could see them still, on fire with green, and could taste the cool trickle of delicious savor in her throat; grasses and more grasses filled with wine.

Balo was a favorite with old Sapor, king of the donkeys. Sapor ruled the corral through the hours of dusk after the sun had left the sky. His master was a Roman, and Sapor had a high respect for law. He was a tall donkey who knew how to say, "Less noise," in a voice that commanded while it seemed to request. They all admired Sapor's sense. "One needn't be an ass at all times," he told the other donkeys, baring his teeth. "We are the most despised of animals but some day the tail will be on the other foot." It was a slightly mixed metaphor but all the donkeys liked it. It turned their minds away from the dirty corral to a future that was green and could be eaten. No harsh masters shouting and using the heavy stave. No dust caking on the hide; but cool streams, soft words, meadows stretching to the infinite horizon.

When a luster of stars came on the sky the donkeys huddled together near the walls of the temple. "Who will tell us a story?" Sapor asked. "The night will be long. The sun is warming himself in the temple for tomorrow's work."

They were all quite good at story-telling. "I once belonged in a great court," a scarred old donkey volunteered. He was so old no one knew his name, and he himself had forgotten it, so they called him Nemo.

"In those days I was young and fat," Nemo continued. "My nose was smooth and polished from eating good corn. No one but princes played with me. Their robes were of gold tissue, pale as the morning sky before the sun comes up. One wore a great ruby on his forehead, because he was the eldest son and must one day rule the kingdom. It was like a rose, and his hands were like rose petals.

"Through the endless gardens we laughed and played. Fountains of gold and silver danced and sang. The woods were musical with thrushes, the hedges and rose gardens were cut in shapes of deer and elephants. There were great pools like carpets of blue spread on the green grass.

"Always the little prince was on my back, or hanging on my neck. He had soft lips and breath like meadow hay. He promised me: 'When I am king, Nemo, you will be my prime minister, for I love you.'

" 'That will be an improvement on what we have,' was the comment of Nicanor the eunuch, a great fat jelly of a man with a laugh like distant thunder.

"One morning my little prince did not come to me. I waited in my cool stall. The gardens were still like death. Even the white peacock forgot to scream as he trailed his thousand eyes along the shrubbery. Finally I heard a sound of wailing. It grew and grew, until it pierced my heart like a sword.

"Then Nicanor came. His eyes were red, his face was scarred with tears. He untied my golden halter and put his fat arms around my neck. 'Now you will never be prime minister, Nemo. The prince is dead, and you are banished from the kingdom. I am banished too. The king does not wish to remember the past.'

"So I came here with Nicanor. But he could not live away from the hanging gardens. He stole back there where the sun is always polished gold, and was put to death.

"I was sold to a fishmonger. Stinking fish were all I knew. I got to recognize every stone in every street of Jerusalem. But one place I never saw, the great golden temple where the sun rests at night."

"I know it quite well," Amarillis said in her lisping accent. She was a donkey delicate of foot, brown like a withered leaf and so well-bred she would eat only one wisp of hay at a time. "My master was a Levite. Many times I heard him speak of the temple. The courts are of gold and silver. There are brazen lavers there cunningly carved and held aloft on the horns of oxen—wide basins in which the purest water rests. They are for the priests who must wash themselves clean before each sacrifice.

"There is a great court for the men, one for the women, another for strangers. More lovely still are the courts for the priests and Levites. They are all flanked with rows of flashing pillars. So wealthy is the spot that seven golden lamps burn there in the bright light of day. On a golden table are flat loaves of bread, crusty and brown but just made for show."

"But where does the sun rest?" Sapor asked.

"Now that's one thing I never heard, come to think of it. My master was so busy he never had time to tell me. I'm sure it must have been in the hidden room behind the curtain woven like the rainbow. The high priest was the only one who ever went there and only once a year. There was a grapevine of solid gold that climbed the arch above the rainbow curtain. The vine had leaves of emerald. The grapes were amethysts, richer than the Roman purple."

"Indeed!" Sapor snorted rudely. "What do you know of that? Have you been to Rome then?"

"No! But I have seen Pontius Pilate sitting on his ivory chair, ringed with the golden breastplates of his guard."

"Pontius Pilate! He is a shadow-king, and poor I can tell you. His purple is faded like a fishwife's shawl compared to Caesar's. After all, I was born in Rome." Sapor lifted his head with some disdain. "That makes me the only citizen of Rome among us. And Rome is the world. It covers seven hills with forests of pillars. Ten times a hundred temples catch the light. Pillars and colonnades mount to the sky. The air is filled with statues of gods flaunting the daylight on the streets below them. The Forum is like molten glass. Everything is sold there in the great shops. I once saw a golden donkey so tiny he was scarce one hand in height. His master touched a diamond button on his back. The donkey danced merrily like a wind-blown leaf and laughed the most melodious laugh. But that is only one of the wonders that I saw."

"Wonders! Wonders!" Balo screamed. "You talk of wonders. But these things are treasures of shadow. Night by night you count them over like the cold stars. They cannot warm your heart or feed your stomach. And when the day comes you will go up and down the rough streets, up and down endlessly. Despite the treasures you cherish, you will have blows of the stave, heavy burdens. The sun will burn you in summer!"

Balo broke off. Her lamenting voice filled the corral. All the donkeys were uneasy. They shifted their feet and looked about with ill-concealed unhappiness. Sapor was the first to recover. He walked over to Balo, stepping softly on the littered ground.

"There, there!" he said, licking Balo's shoulder. "You are right, Balo; of course you are right. But in telling our stories we are not wrong, or only partly so. The hours are long until we must sleep. Come now, my friend, you are the best story-teller of the lot. Tell us why you are sad. We want to hear that story. It is sure to take us into a world of hope beyond Jerusalem. Yes, beyond Rome too."

Balo stopped her crying and moved with Sapor to the middle of the group. A deep sigh broke from her throat. The colt curled up at her feet.

"It is not my story at all," Balo said. "Long ago it

happened to my grandmother, and it all started in Nazareth where I was born."

"What is it like in Nazareth?" Amarillis asked. "I've heard it said no good can come from there."

"Perhaps not," Balo replied. "The good usually stay home. I can tell you that Nazareth was filled with kindly men and women. The town is like steps that walk up and down the hills. The houses are of rough stone but snug and warm against the northern air. In winter the frost turns the trees and fields to diamonds. But in spring and summer it is even more beautiful. The houses are walled in green arches of trees. The air is filled with singing birds, and the sky is so blue it soothes your eyes. Along the hedges the grass twinkles with blue stars that sing when the winds go through.

"Day is long, but tasks are simple ones. If the sun is hot there is always a tree for refuge saying, 'Rest, little one.' In winter there are warm caves knee-deep in fragrant hay. But best of all are the kindly people. They do not shout commands but sing out for us to go or stop. They never use the stave. Sometimes the children bring little honey cakes to us, or sweet-smelling apples red like the morning sky.

"In all the town my grandmother had the very best master. The man's name was Joseph. He had a small shop on the chief road there. From morning to night you could hear him singing the songs of David—

'Lift up, O ye gates! Be lifted up!'—while he sawed the boards and planed them. The children of the town played around him for they liked his singing and quick laughter. The girls would take the shaving curls and stick them under their knotted kerchiefs. How funny they looked with their faces brown as thornberries rimmed with heathen curls!

"My grandmother had a little cave all to herself at night. It was so neat and clean a Roman could have eaten from the floor. You'll pardon me, Sapor."—Balo was bowing—"I meant no harm by that."

"But the Romans are fussy," Sapor said. "I had a mistress once who used to wash my ears with perfume. It made me itch all day."

The other donkeys shook their heads in horror at this, and Balo went on:

"My grandmother was named Altair for the morning star. She was pure silver like her name. Sometimes when the night was dark she counted the stars when she couldn't sleep. But I don't think she ever counted them all. Sometimes, too, if the night was very deep the stars came so close above the town that my grandmother fancied herself among them. The milky way looked like a shining road on which she could walk away to a country of light-filled wonder.

Joseph had a young wife. Her name was Mary. She had a face more beautiful than a blossoming almond tree under the falling moonlight. Each time she dropped her veil for a moment Altair had to look at her from under her eyelids, glimpsing the lovely face with its great liquid eyes that no kohl could help to frame or ornament into more shining beauty. Her nose was so straight and perfect it seemed the work of some Greek master. When she spoke it was like the sea haunting the shore. The heart came alive and the mind reached out to happiness.

Altair never had one harsh word from either of them. Each day they brushed her fur with brushes made of palm frond until it shone like the morning star. She liked, too, the red carpet, thick and soft, that Mary had woven on a little loom that said 'clack, clack' all day long in the garden. Mary made the carpet to cover Altair's back when she was hauling poles and logs from the forest. Never once was her back scarred or sore.

On Sabbath morns Altair's manger was filled to overflowing with fresh meadow hay. Yet Mary would remember something more when the sun was risen. Out she would come to the stable. Folding back her veil, she would bend to kiss the white mark on Altair's forehead. Then her beautiful pale brown hands would loose the red cord on the halter and she would say, 'Go, my little star, where you will. Keep strong and well until the great day ends.'

In the silence of the Sabbath day Altair would

wander in the fields and woods. She drank from the little brooks and learned the language of the daisies who talk all day of love and lovers. But at times her heart drew her homeward, and she would go back there to look over the garden wall, stepping so softly on the grass her hoofs seemed shod in satin from Damascus.

Under the fig tree that threw green and gold patterns on the grass-edged stones of the court were Mary and Joseph. Joseph read from a great scroll bound with crimson velvet. At a little praying table knelt Mary. The soft blue of her gown had fallen back from her wrists. She rested her elbows on the smooth brown wood inlaid with ivory stars, her chin supported in her tapering fingers. Joseph half watched her while he read. The flowers along the wall bowed in reverence. The birds leaned out of the trees to see her face. It was perfect alabaster when the light shines through. 'I'm named after a star,' Altair thought, 'but she is like the moon surrounded with adoring stars.'

Altair knew it well, that little prayer desk where Mary knelt. For generations it had been polished with constant use in Mary's home until it had the texture of copper lamps braised and shining. There were two spots worn almost white by the elbows of those who had knelt there. They were like sunlit patches on the burnished leaves of orange trees, maps of fervent prayer. Altair loved the prayer desk, too, because it called to mind that strange March morning of the same year in Jerusalem.

It was before the time when Mary came to Nazareth to live with Joseph as his wife. Mary was in Jerusalem at her mother's house. It was early morning in Anna's rose-walled garden. Altair was tethered near the sun-warmed wall. Mary knelt in prayer near the table that was part of her dowry. Suddenly all the trees were shaken with a breath of wind. A young man stood there before Mary. There were golden sandals on his feet, and his clothes were a thousand shades of red; they moved in the brisk breeze as if they had been great wings of fire. The young man's face was shining. It glistened as with oil below his blond hair that seemed of gold in the harsh spring light. The noises in the street outside could be heard above the wind.

Because of the rustling of the trees Altair did not hear what the stranger said to her mistress, nor her replies. But Altair trembled from the look on Mary's face. It was like some thousand years of thought turned inward on silence. A shadow of anguish lay about her mouth and eyes. Then Altair heard her voice, smooth as polished marble, strong as bronze, as she said, 'Be it done to me according to thy word.' The young man bowed in reverence. Suddenly the light seemed drained from the sky. The trees were dim sentinels and the golden lilies along the walls were like ghosts of gold, for all the light was in the face and form of the little maiden. She seemed made of glass in which a furnace glowed with prismatic light. It was stronger than lightning, but steady like a flame of fire. Altair's eyes were blinded, and she bent her head against the cool of the wall. When she looked up, the young man had left the garden. The breeze no longer shook the trees and Mary was weeping in her hands.

Always on the Sabbath when Altair had looked long upon lord and lady she would steal away to her stable. Munching the fragrant hay, she would count over her happy hours until the first stars came at night. Then she would give a joyous cry to see Mary and Joseph standing there smiling in the dusk. They would wish her a happy week while they picked the burrs from her legs and brushed her with the broom of palm fronds.

One day a Roman soldier mounted on a dappled stallion came to Nazareth. His helmet shone like sun on water. Sparks cascaded from the hoofs of his horse. The very stones rang with the sound of his approach.

The Roman halted in the market place of many faded tents, for Nazareth is not a rich town. Then he unslung a horn from his shoulder and blew a ringing blast. People came running from the shops and houses; they came across the fields, too, with their robes girt up for greater speed. Soon the tall dappled stallion was surrounded by a sea of faces. The noble horse stood there trembling, obedient to the strong hand clutching the reins.

'What is it now?' The people asked each other. They buzzed like hives of bees until the village elders in their long fringed gowns made a sign for silence.

The Roman shook out a long scroll of finest parchment stamped with massive gold and red seals. In a stern voice he read the Latin lettered there, which Nicodemus, the scholar, translated into the liquid tongue they all knew.

It was amazing news. The high Emperor Tiberius commanded that a census of the people be taken the last month of the year. Each one was to go to his ancestral city that the record there might be set down and sent to Rome. Those who failed to register were to be given a heavy fine. They were to have no further standing before the law.

As the soldier finished his reading, Altair gave a great 'he-haw' that brought a frown to the face of the soldier. His eyes grew small with fury like an angry pig's, while all the people laughed. Then, in the babble of voices that arose, Joseph stepped forward, caught Altair by the collar, and hurried off with her.

Mary was making almond cakes on the kneading table in the garden. Her hands were white with fine flour.

'Yes,' she said at last when she had pondered the

news Joseph told her. 'So the great books say, *In Bethlehem of Juda.* It will be winter then, and we no longer have kinfolk there.'

'But we are both of David's line,' Joseph said. Confidence in this made his eyes shine, as he sought to reassure Mary.

'No matter, Joseph. We are like the birds I think, who neither sow nor reap. All has been arranged on high. Let no finger of fear press upon our hearts. It is written in heaven what must be. The stylus prints upon the wax. The brush fills out the scroll with signs outlasting pyramids and all the storied pomp of Egypt. But beyond all this is One who appoints the stars their places and shakes the waves awake. His will only do we seek and follow.' "

Balo stopped speaking. Her eyes were filled with tears. Cry after cry came from her throat. The other donkeys bent their heads.

"Oh, Balo," Amarillis said at last, "don't leave it there! The Starry Hunter has just shown his head above the hills. What happened then to Mary and Joseph? Tell us, I beg you. Was your grandmother taken up among the stars? There is some great thing hidden here for all of us."

"Amarillis is right," Sapor said. "No story-teller worthy of the name stops when his tale has just begun. Surely you know what Aristotle said: A thing to be complete must have a beginning, a middle, and an end. One doesn't need to be a super-donkey to see that."

Balo stopped crying. "I remember what Altair told me well—only too well." Then she went on:

"The end of the summer came to Nazareth. Then the rains fell, pelting down on grass and trees. The roses died. The thrushes flew away. The fields and trees were stripped and lonely under a wide tent of slate. Storm clouds belled across the sky.

Altair was warm and snug in her clean cave. Joseph was fitting cabinets within the house, and Mary was weaving there before the fire that leaped and crackled on the hearth. The clothes she wove were soft like breasts of eider-duck. While her deft hands threw the shuttle back and forth, her eyes were lost in distance. Sometimes she sang a song, 'My soul does magnify the Lord.'

Then came the last month of the year. Each day Mary herself came to the stable door. Her dress was blue as if a piece of sky had been woven on the wind's looms.

'We are going to David's town, little star,' she said. 'Grow strong! The journey will take us far away from Nazareth. Your strong feet will be weary before we see our little home again.'

Altair could see that Mary was big with child. But what she had told her was all Greek to Altair.

The weather cleared with the first frost. Under a

cloud-filled sky one day Joseph came to saddle Altair, saying, 'It's good, Altair, your coat is thick this year. The hills are cold, they tell me.'

First he put on the red carpet, tying it down snug and firm. On the red carpet he put a thing like a cradle made of wood wound with soft red cloth. Tassels dangled from the ends and brass bells jingled with every motion Altair made. The wine and water skins were hung from the high point of the saddle at the front. There were folded pallets quilted and thick as the coats they wear in far Cathay when snow drifts in the streets like fallen stars. Shawls and cloaks were thrown across the seat, and a great bundle with bread and cakes and thick slices of cooked lamb was tied to the cradle's back.

Finally, Joseph stood before the door with Altair's bridle in his hand. He wore his thickest sandals wound with heavy cloth about the ankles. A thick cloak of gray in many folds fell about his shoulders. It had a hood that tied under his chin and half concealed his face.

'Mary!' he called. She came then, lifting the leather curtain of the door. Altair saw her glancing back for one last possessive look as good wives do.

'I have quenched the fire, Joseph,' she said. 'Everything will be all right, I think.'

Mary gave Altair's neck a gentle pat. She was all swathed in cloaks of woven wool; a veil covered her face up to the eyes. The cradle creaked a song of protest when Joseph lifted Mary up. He tucked a thick brown shawl about her knees and feet.

'Are you warm?' he asked.

'Quite warm, Joseph. Thank you.'

He grasped his heavy shepherd's crook firmly in his hand, and they were off along the southern road, rutted and worn with rain and frost.

Altair had felt herself weighted down with the many bundles. She expected a hard journey through the hills. 'It's little enough,' she thought. 'My life has been without one single care. I know the wisdom of the fields. I can read the hearts of flowers and interpret the song of every bird. These came to me through love. Now I can repay some part of what I owe.'

But it was strange. The very moment Mary settled herself within the cradle the weight seemed light as feathers. Lightness came to Altair's legs. 'You must dance; you must hurry,' chuckled the wine skin to the water jar. Altair danced a step. Her nimble feet trotted.

'Ho, my beauty!' Joseph cried, pulling the bridle. 'There are many hills to climb, Altair, before we get to Bethlehem. Your burden is a precious one. You must not stumble.'

Altair slowed her pace to a brisk walk. 'That's better,' Joseph said. 'Is all well with you, Mary?'

'Yes. All is well,' she said.

They went through the path Joseph knew from his

youth spent in the hills. The distant trees were like
the dark sad mist magicians make to charm the dead.
The breath of Altair and Joseph went out before
them like puffs of gray smoke in the frosty air. The
winter-ruined trees stood everywhere like mounds of
skeletons dreaming of rebirth. Altair saw one bluebird. It flew beside them singing the same song over
and over:

> 'Summer has come to frost and snow,
> The roses shall bloom, the lilies shall blow.'

She is a poor crazy thing no doubt, my grandmother thought, the silly bird, why hasn't she flown
south with all her kind? But the bluebird perched on
every branch. Still she sang:

> 'Summer has come to frost and snow,
> The roses shall bloom, the lilies shall blow,
> And all the world my riddle will know.'

Perhaps she has fallen in love with a rose, Altair
thought. Now she must find her way all alone back to
the south.

But strangely enough the bird seemed merry. She
hopped and flitted and sailed up into the sky singing
her song.

At midday the travelers stopped in a grassy spot on
the side of the road. Suddenly a rift came in the
clouds. A dazzling shaft of sun shot down. It had

warmth in it as when the door of a baker's oven opens. Little flakes of sun frolicked in the air.

Joseph took one of the quilted rolls from Altair's back and threw it on a flat rock. It had specks of gold in it that glittered out a welcome. Then Joseph made a tiny fire of dry sticks and sweet-smelling balsam. It blossomed quickly into flame. Mary dropped her veil and held her hands out to the flame while Joseph warmed the meat. Mary's face was rosy with the cold. Altair, watching her, was too engrossed to pluck the wayside grass. The bluebird, like a spot of sky in a low tree, sang his strange song while the travelers rested.

By nightfall they had come a good distance toward Jerusalem. Altair could not understand why she did not feel tired. A sense of lightness and ease was in her heart. The clouds had flown to their nests on the horizon. The clear evening sky was fired with sunset. It quickly turned to ashes. One last long rosy finger of light pointed to the first star floating in the sky. Joseph was quick to see it. 'It's the evening angel,' he said.

Mary smiled. 'Soon the night will come wherein no man may work.'

'Yes, I know,' Joseph said. His face was anxious, and he tugged his beard. 'We must stop soon. But where?'

'Over the next hill a little. There is a farm, I'm sure. I saw the lanterns twinkling from that high place back there.'

Two great dogs came rushing down. Altair's heart was pounding. How she longed to talk as humans talk, 'Do not fear, gentle mistress, my heels are strong. Hold tight then, while Joseph and I keep off these beasts.'

But when the dogs drew near they stopped. The hair along their necks fell down in place. They lowered their heads. One with a white star on his face came forward. He lifted one paw. Joseph took it. Mary leaned forward to watch. Her hand was warm between Altair's ears.

'Our God is good,' Mary said. 'Even the beasts are kind. How can we fail to find a welcome?'

Joseph, still frowning, seemed to doubt a little as he led Altair up the path to the gate in a low wall. The gate clicked open and a man came out. A lantern of yellow horn shone in his lifted hand. His beard was reddish-gray and he had falcon eyes, yellow and hard.

'The peace of God rest on you!' Joseph said.

'And remain forever,' the man answered.

'My wife and I are going down to Bethlehem.'

'Where do you come from?'

'From Nazareth.'

'It's a good town to be *from*. There are many unbelievers there, and many godless.'

'Perhaps. But we are Jews of David's royal line, my wife and I. We're going down to enroll, because the Romans say we must.'

The man spat. 'The Romans are dogs! We zealots spit on them. Who is Caesar? A demon god corrupting our land.'

'Yes, I know all that. But I am a simple carpenter. I need my work because we live by it. My wife is with child. Shelter for the night is all we ask.'

'Our house is filled with kinsfolk and friends as needy as you are, even worse. They, too, will go to sign their names on Roman rolls for tax gatherers and the Roman vultures. There is no room here.'

Joseph sighed, a sigh that seemed to come from his very sandals. He twitched Altair's bridle, but Mary put her hand along my grandmother's neck in a command to stay.

The latch of the gate clicked again. A thin country woman stood outlined in the yellow light.

'Simon!' Her voice was soft and deep. One work-worn hand touched the sleeve of his long cloak. 'These two are gentlefolk. It's cold tonight, and they are Israel's children like ourselves.'

'But we are crowded now.'

'The house is, yes. But you forgot the hay shed. It's sheltered on three sides. With a fire in the court it will be far better than the frosty hills. Our God has said, *Shelter the children!*'

The man answered nothing. With a half-savage gesture he lifted the latch and Altair stepped up over the broad sill of stone.

The shelter of the farm building cut the wind and

the shadows fell around them. Following the broad path of light in which the strangers walked, they came to the hay shed in the corner of the court. Altair halted with the light. The man set the lantern on the ground, turned abruptly, and walked away.

Joseph lifted his wife from Altair's back. Mary stood firmly on the ground and dropped her veil.

The woman waiting there clasped her hands together. A gentle 'Oh!' puckered her lips.

'My name is Ruth,' she said.

'And mine is Mary. Ruth is a lovely name. It makes me think of harvest time and gleaning golden fields.'

The woman laughed. 'And great faith too. You are welcome.' Her words poured forth like a brook swollen with rain. 'It's true the house is crowded. Everyone is going home to register. My kinsfolk and my husband's. He has more kin than I. And it's his kin that makes him angry. His sister Lea in a Roman dress! That Jezebel! he calls her. Then there are all the cousins, mine and his, who have filled our house like an apple fills its skin. This hay shed is quite clean. The hay is new this year. We barely got it in before the rains. That was the day the ox was sick too, I remember. I'll bring a great pan heaped from the hearth. A fire will warm you while you eat. My husband says I talk too much, and like a bee in a meadow flit about. Perhaps it's true. Now, I have baked fresh cakes today. You're sure to like them . . .'

'I beg you, do not trouble yourself for us,' Mary broke in. 'Our wants are simple. We have bread and meat packed in that roll on Altair's back.'

'It's no trouble, no trouble at all. Never have I seen a lovelier face. If the house were not full, believe me, you would sleep before the fire. Oh me! I do talk long. And you are cold.'

Ruth turned and hurried off across the courtyard to her house. The horn lantern cast its pleasant beams on the cascading hay, golden as honey.

Joseph spread out the quilted rolls. The two dogs came to Mary's knee. She bent down to pat them and scratch their ears.

Ruth soon came back followed by a country boy carrying the dish of glowing coals. 'This is my son Joel,' she said. 'His back and hands are stronger than his mind, because he's deaf.'

The boy's mouth was smiling. His thick lashes covered the windows of his eyes. Back and forth he went bringing bundles of twigs and dried branches that he broke with his great hands.

Soon the flames were crackling. The red rug thrown on the hay was spread with a clean cloth Ruth had used to cover the brown dish of almond cakes. Joel was bringing wattled screens. He placed them in such a way that they made a little room in which the fire was the center, like a warm heart pulsing. It seemed to Altair she had never felt so well and happy. Joseph had rubbed her fur all over until she glowed. Meanwhile the meat was roasting on the coals. The light cast rosy flowers on Mary's face. The two dogs near her on a truss of hay looked at her with deep solemn eyes. Then Joseph blessed the meat and bread. It seemed to Altair an angel stood there saying the words with him.

Ruth hurried back to the house at a shouted cry from Simon. Joel stayed on. His eyes were wide like two stars. Finally, with mumbled words and signs Joel made it clear he would watch the fire through the night. He brought more sticks and settled himself on a rough stool before the fire.

Mary was spreading out the brown shawl on her quilted mat. Suddenly her hands were quiet. She lifted her face. It was smiling. Altair saw a smile more beautiful than all the dawns of summer. Mary walked over to where Joel sat, wearing a smile on his vacant face.

'God keep you for your kindly heart, Joel,' she said. And putting out her hand she touched his cheek. She walked back, wrapped the thick shawl about her, and knelt in the hay. The fire threw dancing tongues of light on her back.

Then Altair noted something strange. Joel was crying there before the fire. The tears were flowing down his cheeks like winter rains washing away the stains of the year. Over and over Altair heard him say the words, 'I hear!' "

~ TWO ~

Balo paused for breath. There were tears in her eyes. "Why was I stolen from Nazareth by evil gypsies?" she complained. "Why could I not have . . ."

Nemo broke in, "By Bacchus! Balo. You can't stop now. I have my lips half gnawed away in suspense."

"It's true," the other donkeys said in chorus. "We must know what happened in the end. Go on, then! Tell us the tale before we sleep."

Balo bent down and chewed a wisp of straw beside her colt. "Oh, what a world!" she sighed.

"Now, Balo," Sapor said, "no crying! After all, you're a grown donkey, and we are a proud race."

"All right. I'll tell the story," Balo said at last. "But you can't make me happy if my heart is sad. Let me see. . . ." And then she went on:

"The further days of travel were mostly without strange events, Altair told me. The air was cold. The paths were thick with mud. They began to be thronged with people going to register their names in their home villages. Yet every night Mary knew where to stop. Her face was coinage that put Rome's gold to shame. Somehow each crowded inn made room for her. She hardly spoke at all. Her mind seemed looking inward, but her face was radiant like a lantern in the hands of a lonely traveler at night walking a haunted road.

By the time they came near Jerusalem, Altair was tired, she said. The roads were better here, but crowded. Donkeys and wagons and beasts she called camels, with necks as long as twenty donkeys and a smell like the valley of Hinnon when they burn the garbage there. Sometimes a Roman chariot rushed by with the speed of wind. The horses were feathered with foam.

It was not her legs that grew tired, Altair said, but her mind and nerves. She tried so hard to protect her mistress in the press of men and beasts. Once they were all forced off the road. A troop of Roman soldiers filled the way. Before them went two brass eagles on a pole above a flying banner followed by rank on rank of men, their feet moving like music. Short swords went 'clank, clank' against their lifted knees."

"Ah!" Sapor cried. "The Roman power. A fine thing for the world, I think."

"I wish you had been there," Balo said. "Down in

the ditch with all the other Jews, while Rome went by with blowing horns."

"Well, anyway, when I left off, Altair's hoofs were deep in the mud. Mary was tilted in the cradle dangerously. Yet Altair heard her laugh and then she spoke the words, 'He has put down the mighty from their seats.'

'It's plain to see,' Joseph said, when they had scrambled up to the level road, 'that the Holy City will be crowded tonight.'

'Yes,' Mary answered. 'It would be cruel to add more mouths to feed. Kindness should not be put to the test. I long to see my mother, as you know, and even more the temple of our God, like a great eagle perched on a mountain top.'

'If we take the eastern road at the next fork we can reach the house of Lazarus before the night drops down from the hills.'

'That's better, Joseph. It will be quiet there in Bethany.'

'And nearer to David's town.'

Joseph led Altair into the farmstead of Lazarus as night was stalking the hills.

'Ho there!' Joseph sang out. He seemed no longer tired.

The dogs belled out a greeting. This was no sound of threat, Altair was sure. Lights sprang up everywhere. Young Lazarus was standing at the gate holding a bronze lamp high. The light fell like fountains on his curly hair and beard.

One glance was more than enough. 'Martha!' he called. His eyebrows danced on his forehead with delight. 'Joseph and Mary have come from Nazareth. Rouse up the slaves and trim the lamps.'

Altair was happy watching what ensued. The greetings and embraces. Water was warmed at the fire to wash tired hands and feet while Martha went like a shuttle through the rooms bringing more lights and braziers bright with coals until the whole house glowed.

Snug in her stable along with the other donkeys, Altair was long awake telling the news from Nazareth. Kobal, the chief donkey, was sleek and fat, the special favorite of his master Lazarus. Kobal was quite severe with Altair when she told the story of the young man she had seen in Mary's garden. 'You should learn to listen better. Then we'd know the full story instead of half,' he said to her.

'But the wind was blowing hard.'

'Nonsense, you town donkeys just don't learn to use your ears. Why, I can tell where the best grass is by merely listening to the sheep cropping a mile away. I know when Lazarus moves the door latch, even though I can't see him.'

'Well, you are wise enough I grant it,' Altair said, 'but I have learned the language of the birds and flowers. I wish you could have heard the bluebird singing:

> "Summer shall come to frost and snow,
> The roses shall bloom, the lilies shall blow,
> And all the world my riddle will know."'

'Winter and summer! It's a silly verse,' Kobal said. 'It's like that prophet who wrote the verse about the lion and the lamb lying down together. I'm glad I'm not *that* lamb. Anyway, poetry is silly stuff.'

It worried Altair that Kobal did not approve of her. She tried to feel sorry about it, but Kobal's droning voice went humming in her ears. The next thing she knew the morning light stood in the stable door.

Altair was glad to see the stable boy with Mary's red rug folded on his arm. He brushed her fur with long swift strokes and packed the bundles on her back. Soon she was standing in the outer court. Martha kept running in and out bringing fresh things to be tied into the large packages. First it was more quilted rolls of lamb's wool, light as feathers.

'The day is cold here in the valley,' Martha said. 'But in the hills the wind will stab like spears. There may be snow.' She scanned the gray sky, frowning. 'I'm sorry our little sister Mary is not here. She's in Jerusalem with Roman friends. Oh yes, I've baked some special cakes. I must get those, and my best winter cloak. It's lined with fox-fur, red and warm.' Her plain face glowed with her concern.

'Now, by the angels!' Lazarus exclaimed. 'Mary

and Joseph have only poor Altair to carry their gear. This is not a caravan of twenty camels, Martha.'

Joseph smiled under his gray hood. Then Mary laughing put one hand on Martha's shoulder. 'We'll soon return, dear Martha. You must not worry. Who made the wind and snow will keep us on our way, safe in His hands. He keeps all things, even as He keeps the sparrow that no one loves. May He keep you a thousand years!' She kissed Martha on both cheeks. Joseph lifted Mary into the cradle and they started down the road to Bethlehem.

The hills mounted, black with cedar trees. The road twisted like a snake, and Altair struggled over the frozen lumps of clay doing her best to move with ease.

Early dusk was falling before they came to David's town. It seemed lonely and scattered, on the breast of the hill. Large flakes of gleaming snow were falling through the purple air.

First Joseph stopped at the walled courtyard of the inn where the side road branches off to Bethlehem. Inside the courtyard Altair saw more fires glowing there than fireflies that haunt the bogs and marshlands of the south on summer nights. Every cranny of space seemed to be filled. Tents of shawls cluttered the open spaces of the court. There was the loud talk of donkeys. Children raced in and out among the tents and awnings playing their games with shrill-voiced babble.

At last the innkeeper came. He had a face like a full moon. His large bald head was covered with a crumpled fur hat. Two worried creases were like knife marks on his forehead. A little girl-child, with a face pert like a monkey, followed him.

'You can't rest here tonight,' he said in a growling voice. 'The inn is full. The town is crowded like a spring dovecote. David's line stays true to David's brood in numbers. In temper, too!' He scratched his head.

'But what can we do?' Joseph cried. There was anguish in his voice. 'My wife is young. She cannot sleep in the cold hills tonight. Her time is almost come. We must find shelter somewhere, somehow!'

Meanwhile Mary had dropped her veil. Altair saw the little girl bend forward like a bow. She was looking at Mary with wide-staring eyes. 'Father!' the child said. 'The old stable where I play I'm Queen of Sheba is dry and warm. No one is there but my pet ox, Jubal. He's young and white, and very tame, too.' The little girl smiled at Mary as she added the last words.

The innkeeper bent his head in thought. 'It's just a cave we often used before the new inn was built. It's better than the hills or open courtyard. I'm sure it's clean because my daughter Veronica loves the place. Her mother died when she was born. Perhaps I spoil her. She's shy with most guests. But I can see she likes your wife.'

'She's beautiful!' the child said.

Joseph seemed to hesitate, but Mary spoke: 'The Queen of Sheba's house will be our palace. What more could we ask?'

Joseph sighed. 'Perhaps, if we could see it.'

'The child will show you,' the innkeeper said. 'I have a hundred things to do.'

Over the edge of the hill the child went running, down a path so steep Altair could hardly keep from slipping. The child was waiting in the little glade below. 'Hurry!' she called. She opened a wide door of rushes in the side of the hill. 'It's dry here. I keep two lamps burning always. Jubal misses me at night and hates the darkness. Bring the little donkey, too. There's a door at the back that leads to the stall where Jubal is. She and Jubal will go well together. Silver and white gold. And their breath will help to warm your wife until I can bring more lights and many coals from the great fire in the center court.'

With the help of the child, Joseph unloaded Altair's back. The child caught the bridle and led Altair along the edge of the hill. She opened another door of rushes. A little lamp burned on a shelf at the front of the stall. In its dim beams Altair could see Jubal. For his breed he was small, and gold-white as the child had said. His great eyes were like beryls in the refracted light, and he gave a soft cry of welcome. The child threw her arms around his neck and kissed his nose again and again. 'I have brought company for you, my general,' she said. 'You must be good or I shall put you out into the darkness. Now I must go fetch the lights and fire.'

Altair was glad to see the child had not been wrong. The stall where she and Jubal stood was wide. It covered one end of the long stable. It was dry and the floor was green with fresh-strewn rushes that reminded Altair of the meadow where she often walked in Nazareth. At the front of the stall wide-spaced slats ran slantwise to the rough stone ceiling, permitting easy access to the hay piled up in fragrant heaps.

Another small lamp stood in a bracket on the wall in the longer part of the room. It was the same size as the one above the stall where Altair and Jubal stood. Altair could not understand what made the big room seem so bright. Then she saw Mary's face. It shone with light like the moon on frosty nights. Mary sat on the edge of the manger. She was unfolding the long bands of soft cotton cloth Altair had seen her weaving during the summer mornings. She laid them, one by one, on the quilted rolls Joseph had spread on the hay in the manger. She seemed unconscious of everything, even of Joseph stepping about the long room, unpacking the food, and setting things to rights.

Veronica soon returned. A servant man followed her with coals and lights.

'Soon,' the child said to Joseph, 'you will be warm and snug because it's dry here. Many nights I dreamed that some day guests would come to my lonely house. Always the dream gave me joy. I did not know why. But now I feel that joy fulfilled.'

She walked to where Mary sat. 'See?' the child said reaching inside her cloak, 'I brought you one rose from my plant. It never bloomed before at this season. I think it must have known that you were coming here.' She held out a perfect golden rosebud. Altair could smell its fragrance in the stall.

Mary took the rosebud and pressed it gently to her lips. 'How sweet it smells! It is like the savor of your welcome, child. One thing I know. Your life has been lonely here in the midst of many people. But never again after this night will you feel shut away from joy. Your heart shall bloom like this flower, though all the world make winter about you.' She put one arm around the girl, then bent and kissed her cheek. Altair saw the dark young face glow with a radiance like forked lightning flashing through the midnight sky. Suddenly the child was beautiful.

Then in silence Veronica helped Joseph prepare the evening meal. Mary would take no food except unleavened bread broken in a cup of wine. The child watched her while she ate, and Jubal and Altair watched her, too, through the wide-spaced bars of the manger.

After the meal was over, Veronica brought a bowl of warm water and a napkin with scarlet fringe. Mary washed her hands carefully. Her eyes were downcast and she seemed far away in another world.

'I must return to the inn,' the child told Joseph. 'Father will wish to see me and have his meal with me. I'm all he has to love. But I'll return to see that everything goes well. Of course, I always say goodnight to Jubal.'

'You are good,' Joseph said. 'The Lord will repay you.'

'No,' the girl said. 'Often I'm not good at all. I don't like sharing things with others. But this I want to do because my heart says, *Yes*. I think that's good at any rate, or better at least than doing things because you have to.' With a quick gesture of her right hand she drew the hood of her red cloak over her head, opened the door, and went out into the night. Through the open door Altair could see the lacing swords of snow in the air. The ground was already white as lamb's wool.

Silence was thick like feathers in the room. Mary knelt on her quilted pallets in the straw. Her hands were crossed on her breast, her head was covered with a veil of white. It cloaked her completely, like the snow hiding the earth outside.

Joseph had spread a pallet near the door. He knelt there like an eagle in its mountain nest scanning the sky.

The silence grew and deepened. Altair said it had nothing of a threat or foreboding in it. It was a stillness warm and comforting like a lovely room in which the householder wakes at night and sees the moonlight drifted thick on the ashes of the hearth in which the warmth still lingers.

How long it lasted Altair could not tell. Jubal, she said, stood like a statue of pale honey. His eyes were opened so wide they seemed ready to fly from his head.

Suddenly Altair noted the growing light. It did not come from the lamps which looked like fading stars in the light of day. The radiance seemed to come from every part of the great room. It was so bright that Altair could see the hammer and chisel scars on the roof and walls of the cave. Still, still the light grew until the air seemed to glow. Then Altair heard the music of voices. It was like the great chorus of singers heard on the festive days in the temple at Jerusalem, but so pure and clear it made Altair's heart stand still with pleasure.

The brightness was dazzling over the outer manger where Mary knelt. Altair could no longer look at it. Jubal had already fallen on his front knees, on the rush-strewn floor. He and Altair bent their heads in the shadow of the low wall, out of the blinding splendor that pervaded the stable.

When Altair looked up again the light had faded. There was a whirring sound in the air like the noise of eagle's pinions. But the flames of the lamps were steady as rocks in a sunwashed desert. Altair rose to her feet and looked out into the manger. Mary still knelt on the straw. She had thrown back her veil. Her face was bent down to a new-born manchild lying on the white cloth spread above the hay. Altair saw on Mary's face a look of joy and adoration such as she had never seen before. It did not much surprise her because the child was beautiful beyond comparison with humankind. In face and form so perfect, he seemed carved by some fabled artist out of ivory warmed to rose and golden lights.

Now Altair found that she could speak. 'Jubal,' she whispered. 'Look! The child is beautiful!'

Jubal with a half-groan pulled himself erect and looked into the stall. He breathed his sweet warm breath on child and mother while Mary, taking up the soft bands like eider-down, swaddled the infant with careful fingers as if he had been made of rose petals.

Then Altair noted another wonder. The hay in the manger had bloomed like the summer grass. It was green again like the parrots that fly through the thick-ranked trees in the rain forest. The flowers in the hay had also found their life. Poppies gave out a ruby light. Cornflowers opened their stars, bluer than the sky. The half-opened bud of gold Veronica had brought was opened full. At its heart was a little crown more beautiful than that worn by any queen.

Joseph stood there, leaning on his shepherd's crook, watching the scene. He seemed waiting for something, and when a noise came at the door at the front of the cave Joseph went to open it. What he saw there made him throw both doors back. The new snow glittered like ten thousand stars in the light of one great star that was so low in the heavens it seemed caught in the branches of the great tamarind trees that clustered around the hill. Voices babbled. There were shepherds standing at the door; many shepherds dressed in their shawls and sheepskins.

'Where is the child?' they asked, in tones of great excitement. 'Oh, let us see this wonder! We are bearing gifts!'

'Let one man speak,' Joseph said, calling for silence.

A gray-haired man stepped forward. His seamed face was like the earth of the road moiled with hoof mark and wagon tracks. The sheepskin on his shoulders was worn and ragged with the cold of many winters. The words fairly tumbled out of his mouth:

'We were in the plain watching our sheep as we have always done. Some slept and some kept watch. Suddenly the sky opened. A great light dropped about us as if the sun had fallen from the sky. There was a shout of trumpets, the clang of symbols louder than thunder. Every man sprang up. We grabbed our staves to fight. Then in the center of the light we saw an angel. He moved like a great flame of fire. His voice was like some sweet-toned bell heard across the golden meadows at the end of the day, as he spoke these words: *Behold, I bring you tidings of great joy that shall be to all the people. For this day is born to you a Saviour who is Christ the Lord. You will find the child wrapped in swaddling clothes and lying in a manger.* While the great angel was still speaking, the whole air flamed to the hills with rank on rank of angels like the sands of the seashore.

'We fell down on our faces at the sight. A burst of song echoed above us: *Glory to God in the highest, and on earth peace to men of good will.*

'When we looked up at last, the angels were gone. "Where does the Scripture say the Saviour will be born?" we asked old Abel, who knows the lore of books and all the moods of the sky.

' "In Bethlehem."

' "But where?"

' "In Bethlehem."

' "But surely there must be something more?"

' "No, that's all there is, my friends," he said. "The prophets were not makers of maps. They merely spoke the words that God put in their mouths."

'How could we hope to find Him? Bethlehem has many stables. There are caves in all the hills. Like men possessed we snatched our gifts and came across the fields, planning to search the town in twos and threes. Then we saw the star. It seemed to rest upon this hill like a great gold shield hung upon a door.

'Strangely enough, we found some other marks as we came on. Flowers bloomed in the snow. The night grew warm like a summer evening . . .'

'The Child is here,' Joseph said. 'Come in!'

They crowded in until the cave was almost full. One boy carried a young lamb in his arms. Some had brought fresh-laid eggs and sheepskins. They piled them at the edge of the manger. They crowded around to gaze upon the child. Mary held him up so all could see him. Hoarse cries of wonder broke from their lips. Old Abel wept with joy that reddened still more his red-rimmed eyes.

Then Altair saw the innkeeper's child skirting the edge of the crowd. There was a look of anger on her face, to see her palace invaded by this rabble from the fields. But when she saw the child in Mary's arms her eyes lit up like two great candles in a holy place. She fell on her knees and clasped her hands together."

Balo paused in a silence of wonder. "All this my grandmother saw. These things I missed by the gypsies' theft! These are treasures the like of which the whole world will never see again!" This she cried out in a voice that echoed back, again and again.

Sapor did not rebuke her. The other donkeys stood in sympathetic silence until Balo fell asleep beside the pale form of her colt.

THREE

NIGHT WAS FALLING on the corral of the donkeys.
The sky over Jerusalem boiled with storm clouds. A
weird green light suffused houses and towers and
made the temple look like terraces of murky emerald. Distant thunder shook the dark hills.

"Where is Balo?" Sapor asked. "I haven't seen her
yet tonight. That Gypsy must be drunk again, and
Balo is probably tied outside some inn."

"You're right as corn," Nabal said. He was a dark
gray donkey, proud of the fact that his master was a
Sadducee. "I saw the three of them late this afternoon.
The water seller was doing a thriving business in the
excitement."

"What excitement?"

"Of course you wouldn't know," Nabal said. "Your
business is with Romans in the upper city."

"Oh, I get around!" Sapor observed. "I saw King
Herod today. He was going down to Tiberias with
all his court. You should have seen him. It was quite
a sight. He wore crimson riding boots, a short Roman
dress of gold, and a tall crown of rubies. His great
black horse, like some spirit of evil, reared and

danced. The people resembled leaves blown about the street, trying to avoid the beast and its rider with the evil eye. And yet some call him 'great.' "

"Those people couldn't have run faster than the crowd I saw," Nabal broke in. "Oh! it was funny. You know how the money changers and the dove sellers have invaded the porches of the temple."

"Yes," Amarillis answered. "And the goods sellers, the candy brokers, and a hundred others mad for gain. It's a disgrace. It makes the whole place worse than a noisy market. They have set up counters and they hawk their wares with voices louder than Damascus does."

"Amarillis is right," Nabal replied. "Today it was a little worse than ever. I could hardly catch the forty winks I usually get. Then I heard a voice that lifted my head as quick as lightning. A strange man stood there on the steps of the portico. He towered above his friends surrounding him. They were a little band, roughly dressed. Their faces were burned brick brown by the weather. But their leader had the majesty and verve of a young god. The dress he wore was purple-fringed like those the rabbis wear. His face was lighted up with flashing indignation. In his strong right hand was a knotted cord.

" 'My house is a house of prayer,' he cried. 'But you have made it a den of thieves!'

"With that he took two strides, like a great scythe cutting the meadow hay, swinging the knotted cords whistling over their heads. It was better than the Greek pantomime we saw in the theater here last year. The sellers ran in all directions. They fell on the stones and crawled between each other's legs. Some were not quick enough to catch up their wares. The tables rolled over; goods went spinning on the stones in all directions. And such screams of injured pride you've never heard! I saw two little beggar boys picking up coins like madmen. They were laughing so hard I thought they'd burst. A great hungry-looking dog went flying off with a leg of lamb. Pigeons were squawking. Some of them got loose and flew up to the roof of the high porch, distracted with the noise.

"The man with the knotted cord swept through the porch like a great wind, and then was gone. Of course a huge crowd gathered. They laughed and shouted in a frenzy until the temple police came with their staffs and beat them right and left. How glad I was to be only a donkey then and not a man!"

"But what of Balo?" Sapor asked. "I thought you said you saw her?"

"I did. But not until the riot was nearly over. She came around the corner led by that evil man in the red turban. The colt lagged on behind. They did a thriving business with all those throats worn raw with squawking. The Gypsy led Balo off toward the Inn of the Three Moons. By this time, no doubt, that water seller has at least two moons under his belt."

"Ssh!" Sapor cautioned. "Don't look! Balo is coming now. The Gypsy doesn't know whether he's leading Balo, or Balo's leading him."

They heard the gate creak, a curse, and a resounding slap. Balo came slowly across the corral, too discouraged to avoid the mud and the dirty water standing about in pools.

"I've saved her nearly all my hay," Amarillis said softly. "She's sure to be sadder than ever. But I can't wait until I hear her finish the story she began last night. One thing is sure. A storm is brewing. The thunder chariot rumbles on the hills. Great flaming angels flash across the sky. We'll all be soaked and cold by morning. We need a good story to cheer us."

"Come!" Sapor ordered. "We must rouse ourselves to flatter Balo if we expect to hear her story. Flattery is the best butter for a wounded heart."

The donkeys gathered around Balo as she came near. The colt was like a moon shadow at her side.

"We could hardly wait your coming," Sapor said in his most formal tones. "Your story last night was better than the sun after a rainy day."

Balo still hung her head and answered nothing.

"I've saved you all my hay, Balo!" Amarillis spoke softly. "The tale you told us has inflamed my mind. I thought of it all day."

"I'm not hungry. But thank you, Amarillis, just the same." Balo moved and gave a piteous cry of pain.

"Balo," old Nemo said, "my time is short here on earth. Please tell me of this child you were speaking about. Perhaps the story's ending may cast light on the dark road that lies before me. Even now the cold spring rain hangs heavy over us all. We'll soon need something that can warm our hearts a little."

"Very well, Nemo," Balo said at length. "My words are slow because my heart is sore. Grandmother told me, over and over, everything that happened. It's a story all the world should know. . . . Now let me see, where was I? My memory is bad tonight."

"You told us how the child was born," Amarillis said. "How I should have loved to see him!"

"I, too, have longed to see him," Balo replied. "When I'm going on my rounds each day I hang my head, but my eyes are looking everywhere. I feel he must come here to the temple. Some day I'll find him and the world will be all right."

Balo paused and then continued. "After the child was born, the stable became a showplace. Shepherds are quiet folk, but no man born of woman can keep a secret."

"Right!" Sapor broke in. "It flatters him to be thought wise among fools."

"Who said those words?" Nabal inquired.

A sly smile wrinkled Sapor's mouth. "None greater than a Roman donkey. I'll give you three guesses and one clue. His name begins with S."

The donkeys laughed, and even Balo seemed somewhat cheered as she resumed her story:

"The great star still lingered on. My grandmother
said it was brighter than the towering lighthouse she
and my mother saw in the harbor of Alexandria. So
low, it seemed caught in the tops of the tamarinds. It
was scarcely less bright in the day than it was
at night. The streets of Bethlehem were crowded with
people looking at the sky, pointing their fingers, and
quick with wrong reasons as to what it meant.

Whole families came trooping out of Bethlehem to
the stable in the hill. 'A lovely child,' some of them
said, then went away. But others are as people always
are. They came to see, but saw nothing because they
could not see. 'Tis they should have our name and
wear a tail.

One woman puffed with eating, and wearing a yellow Roman cloak half her size, hung with a thousand
fringes, came teetering in on high gold sandals.
'There's not much here,' she said to the reed-like man
who followed her. 'It's only a woman and her child.
Where are the angels the shepherds said they saw? I
think the whole affair is the work of some old gossip
hot with wine.' In a whining voice she asked Mary,
'Where are the angels? I'd like to see just one.'

The pert face of Veronica who sat on the manger
near the child flamed with anger like a grass fire. Before she could say a word, Mary put one gentle hand

on the child's arm and replied, 'Angels of God are everywhere. Your guardian angel stands behind you at this very moment.'

The woman turned so quickly, Altair said, that her neck gave a quick snap, quite audible. But seeing nothing there but her reedy husband she exclaimed, 'Come, Jacob! There's nothing here at all! David's town is filled with uncouth rabble; but the wine is good!'

Through those first days Veronica kept begging Mary and Joseph to stay in Bethlehem.

'The child is young,' she urged, 'and the journey back to Nazareth is far too long for him.'

A sad smile lay like a shadow around Mary's mouth. 'Nazareth! I think we shall not see it soon. But I am longing for the day when I present my first-born to the Lord as Moses said. We may stay a day or two until all is done that's written!'

It was not to be. That very night, when all the crowds had gone away, there was a noise outside the door. Joseph looked out through the woven rushes, then said in a loud whisper to Mary who sat on the manger edge fondling the child: 'A group of men is coming here! Some carry swords and spears and they are riding tall camels.' His brow was furrowed, as he wondered what this intrusion could be.

'The time for fear has not come yet,' Mary said. 'Throw the doors wide open and ask them to come in.'

Joseph did as she commanded. Then Altair saw a black tent had been set up in the glade beneath the trees. The great star blazed down upon tethered camels and men in foreign dress whose torches of pitch were burned up in the radiance of the star that poured down in waterfalls of light. One lone man came through the falling silver. He wore a long dress of black banded with gold. About his neck was a heavy golden chain from which a great seal dangled, broad as a man's hand.

'My name is Gandar,' he said. 'My masters are Kings Caspar, Melchior, and Balthazar, who have come from the east, afar off. Night after night, as is their custom, they watched the coursing stars. Then the great star blazed that put all stars to shame. The books said: When that star appeared the King of the World was born. So messages were sent on racing horses, from one to the other, bearing out the prophecies. And each king set out to follow where the star led. All three met under the palms of the desert on a night so bright the palms cast long shadows on the ponds of water. Their joy at meeting was only surpassed by their desire to see the child. After four hours' rest we hurried across the desert once again toward where the great star beckoned. Over the hills and deserts the star led us to Jerusalem. Then it disappeared. We saw the light no more.'

'What happened then?' Joseph asked.

'Without the star we knew not which way to go.

My masters were confused and sad, but being kings they sent me to King Herod's palace to ask direction.'

'What were you told?'

'At first Herod refused to see us. Then a messenger came to say the king would grant us audience. We went into the wide palace court. There Herod sat in his ivory chair on a high dais. His purple robes rippled down below his sandaled feet. Around him were his courtiers and the temple council of gray-bearded rabbis, with the high priest, in his golden breastplate and crescent cap, presiding. My masters told King Herod of the great star and the prophecies in our ancient books. He pondered their words, fondling his ivory staff in which a ruby glowed like a great drop of human blood.

' "King of the World! I'm sure the Romans will be interested to hear that. There's something in our books, I'm sure. Where will he be born that is to be the great messiah, King of the Jews?" He asked the rabbis.

' "The prophets say," the high priest answered, "in *Bethlehem of Juda.*"

' "The prophets, hmmm!" A viper smile twisted the old king's lips and then his face was bland as curds.

' "Does it say *where* in Bethlehem?"

' "No place is given."

'The king thought awhile, and then said to my masters: "You say you saw a star, but now there is none. Many see lights and portents in these days. Most of them are like the imaginings of women. However, you are masters of the wisdom that's in the stars. It may be there's a grain of gold in your search. Go down to Bethlehem. Seek out the child."

'He paused. A dark shadow went across his face like the wing of a vulture. "I, too, must see this king of kings and do him reverence. Come back to me and bring me precise word where I can find him. Your sudden appearance here has made me seem lacking in the hospitality a king owes his brothers."

'He laughed, like sleet falling on bronze. "When you return I'll make up for my lack of courtesy. Here we have dancing girls and all the delights that kings can savor best. Rest here awhile. Enjoy yourselves before your long journey back to your kingdoms."

'In such words he dismissed us. When we came outside the city walls we noted several men on horses following us. They were disguised as travelers, but my masters felt sure we were being followed. We set up camp along the road and rested. No star had yet appeared. Our nosing spies lingered on awhile and finally turned back. We saw them laughing, and one man tapped his head.

'But when we drew near Bethlehem the star beckoned from the sky, like a great angel, and led us to this place.'

'You have done well,' Joseph said. 'The child is here!'

Gandar motioned toward the black tent where the men were waiting. Suddenly the star faded out in the trees above the glade, like an extinguished light blown out with a single breath. The torches were re-kindled. They surrounded the three kings with a ring of fire. The fiery ring opened up at the stable door. A tall man came forward. He wore a crown of golden spikes, each topped with an emerald. A great cope of silver trailed behind him on the floor. Mary held the child upon her lap. The white veil framed her face. The child was smiling as if someone had dangled a tinkling bell before him.

The tall man fell on his knees and kissed the floor. Then rising up he kissed the knee of the child. In his hands he held a white ivory dish filled with gold coins to the brim like the richest honey. This he gave to Mary, for her son. He rose and stood to one side.

A stout snub-nosed man dressed in a robe pow-dered with flower patterns took his place. On his head was a purple turban with a single diamond. He made the same homage, then offered his gift. It was a box of silver filagree, so exquisite it seemed only the frost could have woven it. A wide smile lighted up his face, dark as the wood called ebony. He opened up the box and took out one grain of the gums it held and dropped it in the flame of the little lamp. All at once the stable was filled with the smell of roses and the scent of ginger.

The third king came, bowed down, and offered the

child a flask carved from one great turquoise. 'It is myrrh,' he said, 'combined with other gums for healing. No surface wound can withstand its power.'

The three kings sat on ivory stools before the manger, their gaze constantly fixed upon the child. The courtiers in turn paid their homage and left their gifts. One had brought a little silver horse with a tail of real hair, as a plaything for the child.

The three kings, Caspar, Melchior, and Balthazar, asked many questions of Mary and Joseph. They voiced a strong warning against Herod because of the strange way in which he had received their news about the child. Then Melchior rose and bowed, saying, 'We are wearied with travel. After a short rest we will return.'

Slowly, in great state, they took their leave, ringed by the flaming torches, until they reached the black tent.

Mary disposed the child for sleep, holding him close against her in the straw. Jubal looked down upon them lying there, and if an ox can smile, then he was smiling. Joseph knelt for a moment on his pallet on the floor; after which he fell asleep at once.

The peaceful silence in the stable did not last for long. Sometime in the middle of the night a noise was heard at the door. Joseph dashed the sleep from his eyes and kindled one bright lamp from the dim flame beside the stall. When he opened the door Altair saw the three kings standing there. All wore long hooded cloaks of white. Behind them in the dark glade men moved about without one single light.

'Joseph,' King Caspar said, 'each of us had a dream within the night warning us not to go back to Herod. Evil's afoot, and it concerns the child.'

'I know!' Joseph said. 'This night an angel came to me in sleep and said, *Take the child and his mother and flee into Egypt. Herod desires the life of the child.*'

Mary was sitting by the manger, holding the infant in her arms. 'Talk softly,' she said. 'He is asleep.'

The kings came once more to glance at the child. 'How sweetly he sleeps!' King Caspar whispered. 'Little he knows the evil that stalks through the world.'

Mary pondered the words. 'Our times are in the hands of God,' she replied. 'May He keep you on your way and bring you safely home!'

Hurried good-bys were said. All the while the child slept.

When the kings and their train had departed from the glade, Joseph closed the stable door. His face was grave. 'Mary,' he said, 'this spot no longer affords a safe refuge. We have fulfilled the commands of God and Caesar. Every moment here is fraught with danger. We must depart at once.'

She looked down at the face of the child and bent to kiss him. 'You have said well. We must return to the house of Lazarus for the naming of the child.

Then I must wait my time until we can present him to the Lord.'

'But Herod's threat! It wrings my heart to think of what might happen.'

'Who knows us here? Not one; or where we came from. The star is gone. And like the star we can go back to the unknown ways that God has marked for us. Hurry then, and rouse the little girl. I'll let her know the child's very life depends upon her silence.'

Veronica did not shed one single tear. She kissed the child and helped Joseph pack the things on Altair's back. As she was leaving, Mary gave Veronica a fine gold chain of small linked crosses, that someone in the king's caravan had brought.

'But one more thing,' Veronica said. 'May I have one of the swaddling bands the child has worn?'

Mary shook out the fleecy square of white and gave it to the girl. A piercing sadness made Mary's face look old. 'Some day,' she said, 'this cloth will bear another likeness that all the world may remember how beautiful kindness is.' Mary kissed the child and stroked Jubal's nose.

They fled through the night, Altair recalled, like criminals hunted by hounds.

At the house of Lazarus Altair was stabled once again. There she stayed during the time the child was taken to Jerusalem to Anna's house for all the rites Moses commanded. A horse-drawn litter, closely curtained, carried the three safe from prying eyes and the tittle-tattle on the road.

Altair was worried while they were gone. She saw in that night of flight how heavily the angel's command to fly to Egypt weighed upon Joseph. Suppose Herod captured the child? Going to Jerusalem was like walking into the very jaws of the lion.

She told her fears to Kobal. 'In big towns the people are bored. Gossip fills up the empty hours. Small talk of this and that. No one is safe from the eye, much less the clacking tongue.'

She didn't expect Kobal to agree with her. 'You little know,' he said, 'how wise my master is. Just remember he's with them. And Anna's house is quiet because she prays so much. You donkeys from little towns talk over hedges. In Jerusalem it's not the same. I doubt that you will ever get to Egypt or see the tall pyramids that touch the sky.'

Yet Altair's heart was not happy. The days seemed like a thousand years and all the free pleasures of the fields of Lazarus could not allay her fear.

Then, when the forty days had passed, though they had returned, Altair's fears were renewed. Once again, in the middle of the night, she was awakened. It was Joseph, not the stable boy. Joseph gently pulled Altair's ears as he had always done, and whispered, 'We go to Egypt, now, this very night. Danger is near. Move quickly. Every moment bays like a hound on our heels.'

So quietly they moved, Kobal did not awake. In fact he snored in the stall through all the packing. Altair had all she could do to keep from laughing. For once, she thought, Kobal can't play the oracle.

There were no lights in the courtyard when they left. Farewells were whispered. Mary was weeping. 'All those children slain by the wicked hand of Herod!' she cried. 'Now, the words of Jeremias are fulfilled:

> 'A cry was heard at Rama,
> There was weeping and sore lament.
> Rachael wept for her children;
> She would not be consoled
> Because they were no more.'

Martha could only wring her hands.

'Travel by night,' Lazarus cautioned, 'and rest by day.'

'That was my plan from the first,' Joseph said. His lips were drawn together in a thin line like the stylus makes on the wax tablet.

Day after day they hid in the darkness of the woods. Somehow they always found a spot where the grass was thick. The little field mice came in a ring to watch them camp. Altair heard their chattering talk, 'Rest, little child, and sleep.' The interlacing branches were like sheltering arms about the fugitives. The birds were everywhere. They did not sing, but made soft chirping noises. Joseph would watch for a while; then his head would nod on his crouched knees.

But once the shadows of the night were black, Altair was hurrying down the road toward Egypt. At every hill Joseph would look back on the road behind and say, 'There's no one yet—thanks be to God!' Mary said nothing. Altair felt sure her heart was still sad because of all those children Herod had put to the sword, but she found great comfort in the unclouded face of the child. He seemed to sleep most of the day, but when he woke and nursed, his face was smiling like the morning sky when the sun turns all the hills to.gold.

One day, while they were searching for a place to hide in the forest, a fox came up. Then he trotted forward and nodded his head as if he wished to speak. 'I think he's telling us to go deeper into the trees,' Mary said to Joseph. They went forward in the direction the fox had taken, and behind the thick-laced rows of trees they made their camp. They had barely settled down in the dim morning light when Joseph heard trotting horses on the road.

Two soldiers came by, scanning the trees on either side of the road. The fox stood there, his eyes like amber, looking at the child. No muscle moved; he might have been made of bronze. After a time of breathless waiting the soldiers returned, still looking along the road. Then the fox trotted off.

'They search for us,' Joseph whispered. Mary held her finger on her lips. The child was fast asleep.

That night when Altair took to the road she had a sense of foreboding. The sky was dark with clouds. No moon was visible; the great ship of light sailed unseen.

In the depths of the valley where the road dipped there was a sudden noise. From the blackness three men on ponies rode into view. Their cloaks flew out behind them. A small avalanche of stones rolled down in the narrow way to herald their advance.

The leader of the band jumped from his horse. A curved sword was in his hand. Altair stood still. The clouds above parted. The moon sent down its glitter on the sword and showed the face of the robber chief. He was hardly more than a grown child but his face was wolflike in its profile. Suddenly there came a gurgling cry of joy from the child, who had awakened. At this the robber chief seemed to hesitate.

'These are simple folk like ourselves,' he said at last to his companions. 'There's not much gold here.' Turning to Joseph, he asked, 'Why do you travel at night and not in the daytime with a caravan?'

Joseph was pondering his reply when Mary spoke. 'King Herod threatens the life of my child. His soldiers, two of them, are even now on the road searching for us.'

'Herod!' the man cried. He spat upon the road. 'May God and Satan blast him! If it were not for him I would be sitting in my house this very night with my mother and sisters. Have no fear of us. We're here to rob the rich.'

The robber laughed a high-pitched whinny like a horse sensing the nearness of the stall. 'Here's sport,' he said to his fellows. 'Those soldiers must be well supplied with silver. Horses and swords will bring a pretty penny too. And even clothes. Without a doubt they've made their camp along the road. By this time sleep has caught them. We'll pluck them like two chickens hanging in a market and send them back to Herod wearing a skirt of fig leaves like our mother Eve.'

He spurred his horse. 'We'll catch them while they sleep. You are not far from Egypt, lady. Health to you and the child! Remember me, my name is Dismas.'"

FOUR

"After that," Balo continued, "Altair hurried through the night. When dawn dropped its rose leaves in the morning sky, they were in Egypt. Joseph bent down to kiss the sandy soil. The child awoke and laughed.

A little distance farther on, where a grove of palm trees made a large square of lifted fans, Joseph set up a tent of quilted cloths for Mary and the child.

'Here we will rest awhile,' Joseph told Altair, releasing her from her burdens. 'Now you are free to roam. Don't stray too far!'

Altair was well content. Coarse grasses, like patches of worn carpet, covered the sand in tufts. Of these she soon had her fill. Here, once again, she saw the bluebird sitting on a branch of a low tree covered with red berries. The bluebird preened herself and watched her image in the brown pool, like a piece of lapis caught in a bronze ring.

'Come,' Altair said. 'Sing me again that song of summer in winter.'

'Song lasts a day,' the bluebird replied, lifting one

wing delicately, and then confided, 'Beyond this place is the great floor of sand that stretches to the sky.'

'I have strong legs.'

'You'll need them. The sand is deep. It will pull like hobbles on your ankles. All day the sun burns like a pitiless fire in the sky. Then night falls suddenly like the crack of a whip, and the cold settles down. Sometimes the wind lifts up the sand in showers. It stings the face like bees. Travelers huddle in their tents praying while the fine sand sifts into the hair and beard. Yes, into the brows and the eyelashes until the eyes smart, and breathing becomes painful.'

'I thought Egypt was a fertile land,' Altair said.

'It is, but only where the great river moves like a dark snake sliding through the palms and meadows.'

'I've known many donkeys who have traveled there but not one told me these things!'

'Travelers are all the same. They save the bright things like misers hoarding gold.' "

The noise of Sapor's gusty laughter broke in on Balo's story. "What a wise bird that was! Men are all the same. They love to make the whole world jealous with the sights they've seen. I remember once . . ."

"Now, there you go!" Nemo complained. "You're just like all of the others. Wait awhile! You'll have your turn to spin your monologues. Let Balo go on, or by my prince that died I'll forget the manners I learned in the court and let my heels speak up."

"Any man can make a mistake," Sapor replied. "But few can admit it. I'm sorry, Nemo, I broke in like that. That wise bird touched me in a funny spot. I quite forgot myself."

"I accept your apology," Nemo said. "It is of silver until your silence makes it gold. Balo, go on. What happened then?"

After a moment of reproving silence, Balo went on with her tale:

"Altair was frightened by what the bluebird told her. 'How shall we cross this desert place?' she asked.

'You could join some caravan,' the bluebird suggested. 'But that costs money, and the pace is swift across the desert tracks.'

'Ah!' Altair said. 'If I had wings!'

'You have.'

Altair looked over her shoulder, wondering if she might have grown a wing or two by miracle. The bird gave a trilling laugh to see her glance.

'I did not mean that you had wings yourself.'

'What did you mean?'

'That you could have the use of mine.'

'But how will you load us all upon your back?'

'It wouldn't be a compliment if I called you a bird-brain,' the bluebird retorted. 'I'll use my wings and eyes for you. It's like this: From where you stand the

earth looks like a dish whose edges brush the sky. Even if you had eyes like the lion or the speed of the ostrich you would see only the rim of the dish. With me it's different. In my high flight I see the earth curved like the breast of a brown dove. Each track and blemish shows far beyond your sight. I'll fly ahead and show the way. Then you can go the shortest route between the water holes.'

The bird flew off to the highest palm. She perched there, scanning the sky and eating locusts.

That evening, when the fires of many caravans had been lighted under the restless palms, Altair returned to Joseph's makeshift tent. Mary sat before the tiny blaze holding the child, who smiled to watch the dancing flames. Soon she saw Joseph picking his way among the scattered tents. He carried a squat black jug of milk, and cakes of sun-dried dates. Behind him came a skinny youth with the water skins, like two great bubbles, slung across his shoulders.

'I missed you, little star,' Joseph said to Altair. Then setting down his burdens on the mat, he indicated where the boy should place the water skins inside the tent. 'This is Hakar,' he said to Mary.

As Hakar bent down near Mary, to enter the tent, she noted a great sore on one swollen arm, like a poisonous flower. The boy was conscious of her glance.

'Some months ago,' he explained, 'while I was skinning a calf that had died of some strange sickness I

cut my arm with my knife. It never healed and now
it pains me more every day.'

'It looks quite angry,' Mary said. 'Wait a minute!'
She rose and Joseph took the child from her arms
while she fumbled in one of the bundles in the tent.
'Ah, here it is!' She held in her hand the flask of precious myrrh King Balthazar had brought to Bethlehem. With careful fingers she tilted the flask so that
the myrrh from it covered the sore; then she bound
the arm with a strip of fine cloth she used for swaddling bands.

'Thank you,' Hakar said. 'Your child is beautiful.
Too bad our caravan is moving north and you are
going south. You'll need protection, or at least a
guide to cross the barren land.'

'We have a guide.'

'A good one, I hope.'

A smile lifted the corners of Mary's lips, like the
moon's crescent. 'He guides the stars and keeps the
tides. He knows the path of the moon along the waters.'

Hakar looked at her puzzled, and yet with a kind
of awe in his gaunt face. Then he felt his injured arm.

'How strange! All the pain has left it.' He raised
the cloth covering the wound, then pulled it off in a
kind of frenzy. 'The sore has gone completely! It's
gone! It's gone!' His head bent forward like that of
a crane searching for frogs. 'What remedy is this you

are carrying in your poverty? The rich would pay ten times their weight in gold to know the secret.' His eyes feasted on the flask, like two hands reaching out to clutch it. He turned and walked away with a springing step, as though he wanted to run but feared to do so.

When the moon was like a great brooch on the bosom of the sky, Mary put the child in the tent. Altair watched her for a long time. She knelt there above the boy as if she were lost in a thought too beautiful to leave. Then she lay down and held him in her arms. Joseph was stretched out near the fire.

Sometime before the moon had set, Altair heard a stealthy step. Joseph was sleeping on the quilted rug beside the glowing embers. Straining her eyes, Altair saw Hakar crouching near the tent. She would have cried aloud in warning as he entered but something held her back. The boy was searching about in one of the rolls. Altair heard a quick-drawn breath of satisfaction. The boy was standing clear of the tent. He held the flask of precious myrrh in his hands. Hakar opened it with one swift movement.

'Empty!' he cried, half aloud. He turned the flask upside down and shook it, and dropped it near the tent as if it had been a live coal. Then he raised his clenched fists toward the moon, and in the pale light the sore on his arm showed red like a poisonous flower. A smothered howl broke from his lips. He turned and ran like a man possessed.

Early in the morning Joseph rose and saddled Altair. The stars still burned in the sky. After a brief meal of dates and curds, Joseph folded the tent, lifted Mary into the cradle, and put the child in her arms. Then he saw the flask lying in the sand. 'What's this!" he exclaimed.

'It must have fallen from the roll while we were packing,' Mary said. 'And there's the stopper lying nearby. It's sad to think that our precious gift is lost. How quickly it healed the boy last night!'

'But it's almost full,' Joseph answered. 'It fell slantwise on the tuft of grass among the purple flowers. I must be more careful in the future.' Joseph wound the flask with cloth and put it in the leather pouch that hung from his waist.

When they made their departure, caravans were leaving for the south, taking the well-defined camel track. Joseph led Altair along it for some distance. The horizon seemed hung with yellow silk.

'The morning is beautiful,' Mary said. 'The day star has risen out of the east.'

At this moment Mary saw the bluebird. The tiny creature flew close to Altair in slow circles, then went to the side and settled on a low bush. She did this several times, flitting, flying, and hovering like a hummingbird on a rose.

'Joseph!' Mary said, 'the bird, have you noticed it? It's trying to catch our attention.'

'Yes, it seems to say we should turn that way. But

how can we trust the good sense of so small a creature?'

'Ravens fed Elias in the wilderness and Balaam's ass once pointed out the way and talked as humans do. Why should we doubt?'

Joseph gave no answer. He felt Altair straining at the bridle in the direction of the bird and let her go where she would.

The first day the bluebird brought them through the walls of burning sun to a place screened by tall hills of sand. A single palm threw shadows on a bright pool rimmed with lush grass, greener than the first down of wheat on the furrowed fields. A clear spring bubbled there.

Mary was delighted with the place. She bathed the child, laughing to see him splash the water with his tiny hands. Meanwhile the bluebird sat and sang a song that would have shamed a nightingale. The night came. The deep sky was heavy with stars like a king's treasure chest spilled out on the floor of his treasury. Joseph sat long before the fire. The velvet-covered scroll was unrolled on his knees. Mary looked alternately at the marching stars and the face of the child.

Night after night it was the same. The bluebird led them on through quiet places. One morning when the sun was high they saw in the far distance, rimmed with living green, a city that spread its patterns on the sand. Straight silver lines of calm canals. Temples and houses flaming in the sun. And everywhere the palms dancing across the landscape like David danced before the Ark.

The bluebird flew nearer and nearer, circling and singing. 'My task is done,' she chirped to Altair. 'The way before you lies clear. Even a man can see it. My mate is waiting for me in the high palms along the braided river. There we will make our nest and raise our young.'

Altair noted that Mary seemed to understand. She caught the child's hand and lifted it in a gesture of farewell. The bird flew straight up until its blue faded into the blue sky.

The first day and night in Memphis they camped beside a wide canal in the outskirts of the city. Its waters were purple with the reflection of imperial vines that looped the stone walls and climbed everywhere on the rocks and trees. Joseph left Altair to graze along the grassy banks.

'I must find a house where we can live,' he told Mary. 'Surely in a city as vast as this there must be many places. The gold King Melchior brought the child cannot last forever. In cities they say gold has wings. It doesn't run away. It flies. And I am anxious to set up my shop. There must be many things to make where men crowd together.'

'Our Father guide you,' Mary said.

After Joseph was gone Mary put the child on a soft mat in the shade. She shook the sand-filled rugs and washed the pads and cloths, beating them with a ring-ing sound on the stones. Then she spread them on the grass and bushes. Altair stood near the child, mean-while, cropping the grass and watching the play of dancing light and shadow on the child's face, more beautiful than a great diamond cut without a flaw.

She heard a rustle in the grass. It was a velvet ser-pent coming through, weaving and sliding toward the child. Altair was prepared to scream and use her trampling forefeet. The serpent lifted her wedge-shaped head.

'Peace!' she hissed. 'I'm not here to harm the child. Long ago, my mother told me, some evil thing went masquerading in our skin. It was in the middle of a garden where a glittering tree was loaded with golden apples. Great harm was done to men in our name. Since then all men make war on us. But now this child shall heal many things. I wish to look at him for one brief moment.'

'I have not heard it told,' Altair said, 'that the word of a snake could be trusted. There's a proverb some-where that warns man not to warm a serpent in his bosom.'

'Words cannot harm us,' said the snake. 'It's sticks and stones we fear. See? I won't go nearer. I'll just stay here and raise my head. Ah!' she hissed, 'he's more beautiful than mice, brighter than the sun on the hot stones. Thank you, sir ass. I am content.' Her beady eyes glittered.

'I've heard that snakes are blind or nearly so,' Altair observed as the snake slithered among the grass and reeds and swam off through the water. 'Sir ass, she called me. Now that's a tale for my grandchildren who will not think all serpents are as wise as some men say.'

Joseph returned at nightfall. 'I have not found a single thing,' he told Mary. 'The city is crowded everywhere.'

So it went on for many days. Joseph grew worried. He tugged his beard continually, and looked quite worn.

One morning Mary said, 'Perhaps we should go with you today while you are searching.'

'But the town is filled with people. Roman chariots and the lighter wagons of the Egyptians rush madly through the streets. The narrow walks are crowded. Some harm may come to you or the child.'

'Have faith in him,' Mary said. 'Kings came across the world to greet him and offer him homage. See how sweetly he smiles? Like the summer sun.'

Joseph, too, smiled with the baby. Soon Altair was on the road paved with large blocks of granite that hurt her feet. Joseph pulled one of Altair's ears, saying, 'I know the road is hard. But we'll go slowly. You'll get used to it after a while.'

Altair was amazed at what she saw. The whole landscape was bathed in flowers along the road. The palms were like tall queens decked out with beauty in the courts of Solomon. The pace was slow. Brown men and white and black crowded the footpaths. Many wore the Roman dress of white, but there were a thousand colors shining and changing below the gigantic columns of cobalt, crimson, yellow, and umber that flanked the blank gray walls of the temples. In the distance the Nile showed green as the opal stone. Red sails flashed back and forth like birds, and the noise of whirring water-wheels and fountains filled the air with soothing music.

By the time the full heat of the day closed like a hot hand over the city Altair was tired. The little group had stopped a hundred times. Everywhere it was the same answer. 'There's no place here. Perhaps in summer, if you ask again. . . .'

Joseph led Altair to the edge of a calm garden flanking a temple wall. Mary sat on a marble bench beside a shallow pool. While she was sitting on the bench with the child, Mary noticed a long arcade built on the outer wall of the temple.

'Look, Joseph!' she exclaimed. 'Over there are little shops and signs. Perhaps we might find something among them. It's not far across the garden; the walk will do me good. After that Altair can rest a little, if we must return to the edge of the city once again.'

Joseph gave a deep sigh. At every shop in the arcade he stopped and in the halting Greek of the people asked his questions.

'Is there any place for rent?'

'Not here. Perhaps you'll find something next door.'

Halfway along the row a fishmonger had his shop. Great slabs of carp seemed made of ivory; eels and scarlet prawns were everywhere. The man in charge was black as pitch, but his smile was wide and cordial.

'I have no place,' he said. 'And even if I had, the smell would make you sick. I can't live here myself.' He tapped his long curved knife on the slab. 'But I did hear sometime yesterday, I think it was, that the gypsy at the end of the row takes people in. She's a strange woman!' He snickered to himself. 'She claims to read the future, but I doubt it. If I could read the future I'd never live here and sell fish. I'd just go down to the street along the river where every sailor and Roman fool gambles for gold.' He licked his thick lips. 'Umm! In two months' time I'd have a villa and live like Caesar!'

'You say the gypsy lives at the end of the row?' Joseph asked.

'Yes. In the shady angle of the wall. It's cool there, too, in summer. Many silly Roman women come there to see her about their hopes and loves, but most of the time she goes out along the river streets to find her culls.'

'Thank you,' Joseph said. 'We're fairly worn with looking for a place. We'll go there first.'

A striped awning jutted out above the gypsy's door and made a shade beyond the arch of the arcade that ran to the angle in the wall. The door was rimmed with the signs of Zodiac. Before the door a miniature sphinx of the cheapest plaster crouched.

'I hope we'll find her in,' Joseph said. 'Ho!' he called, stepping beneath the awning.

In the dark square of the door a woman appeared. A scarf of silver was wound again and again about her hair. It made her head look like an enormous melon covered with ridges of wrinkles. Two black eyes bulged in her face above a nose so tiny it seemed lost like a hill in the mountain of her cheeks. She wore a long black robe embroidered with silver stars.

The woman spoke. 'You come to seek wisdom of the stars?' Her voice was deep like a man's. The dramatic gesture she made with one arm showed many silver bracelets one above the other clear to her elbow.

'No,' Joseph answered. 'We did not come to ask the wisdom of the stars. I understand you have some rooms for hire here. That's why I came. This is my wife Mary. We have traveled here from a great distance.'

The burning eyes examined the three and Altair. 'There are two rooms here that are vacant. But who shall have them, I ask the stars to tell me. I can plainly see you are of David's people. You come from the north and have been long on the road. Some danger must have threatened you, I think. Come, let me see your child!'

Mary lifted the fine cloth from the boy's sleeping face. The gypsy woman drew back. Then she bent down. Her lips were pursed together. 'Oh, the beautiful child! How lovely he is! Never have I seen a baby half so beautiful!'

Mary saw the gypsy's eyes were filled with tears, as she said, 'All my life I longed for a child. The stars were unkind. I made pilgrimages to all the shrines and asked the help of the gods. I dreamed of children and when daylight came I longed to dream again. But such a child as this I never hoped to see!' She paused, and then spoke in normal tones in a voice that was musical and kind. 'My name is Candace, after the great queen.'

'And mine is Mary. My husband's name is Joseph and the child's is Jeshua.'

'Now we all know each other, at least by name. That's good. I have two rooms at the back of the house and you may have the use of my garden too. It's small but pleasant.'

'But what must we pay?' Joseph asked. 'Perhaps we cannot afford it.'

'Pay? Oh, give me what you can well spare; you need not pay now. I make myself a good living among the idle ones who haunt great cities. They want a word to tell them what they already dream or hope, or have made up their minds to do.'

'You are good to take us in,' Mary said.

'Not good.' The fat hands fluttered. 'Perhaps sometimes you'll let me hold the child. I'll be careful of him as if he were a fragile flower.'

'He's not fragile at all,' Mary replied, 'but very healthy. You should feel his grip on my thumbs while I'm bathing him, and see how he splashes the water with delight.'

'Come in! Come in!' the gypsy said. 'This is the costume for my public. I'll take off these red shoes. They pinch my feet, and this robe binds me underneath the arms. I'll find an easier dress.'

'Peace be on this house!' Mary said.

'May it return to you!' the gypsy answered, taking Mary's hand and leading her through the door.

Joseph took Altair around the corner of the house. The garden was small. A male donkey stood there near the low wall of wooden poles.

'It's plain you'll have company here, Altair,' Joseph said. 'I wonder what his name is.'

Altair saw the strange donkey watching her. He kept wrinkling his nose as if he didn't know just what to think at the invasion of his privacy.

Under the temple wall a shadow of coolness fell along the curved garden paths. The gypsy came out while Joseph was unloading the rolls and traps from Altair's back. Altair said she hardly recognized the woman. The silver turban was gone from her head. Two wide braids of hair, prinked out with a scarlet ribbon, hung on her shoulders. She wore a loose gown of thin flowered stuff wide enough for a tent. Her feet were bare.

'You see I have a donkey too,' she said. 'His name is Sagittarius. He wanders off, but somehow he's always here when I want him.'

'He's a fine beast,' Joseph replied. 'So slim and sleek. He and Altair . . .'

'Ah! She's named for a star then? That's a good omen too.'

'Yes, they are both silver like the stars. I've had to neglect Altair for some time now but I'll brush her until she shines again. And, soon, I would like to resume my carpentry.'

'You can set up your work bench here in the garden,' Candace said. 'There's room enough for that, and the child can play here, too. Your wife likes the rooms very much. They're not big, but I'm sure you'll find them comfortable, and you can borrow what you need from me.'

'Thank you.'

'Now that the summer's coming you'll be glad there's sun here only in the morning. By afternoon the walls throw a welcome shade. Sometimes in winter I find it a little damp. But most days it's quite bearable and pleasant.'

'I'm sure it is,' Joseph responded. 'I shall be glad to get to work. I've worried so long. Work is the best medicine for that—and prayer.'

Mary stood in the doorway with the child. 'It's pleasant here, Joseph,' she said. 'The rooms remind me a little of our house in Nazareth.'

'Call it your home!' Candace exclaimed. 'It will be, you'll see.' She held out her arms and Mary placed the child in them.

'See how he looks at me, so grave and beautiful? My heart is quiet like the long pools beside the temple of Ra. I feel that this child can teach me to be happy.' Saying this, she kissed him, and Jeshua smiled at her.

Altair was pleased with her new home. As the days went on she saw how content Mary and Joseph were. Altair half-forgot the green fields of Nazareth in the new land of flowers. This was partly because of her growing friendship with Sagittarius. In spite of her first impression, she found Sagittarius both kind and merry. Some nights they wandered to the river bank and had their fill of sweet-fleshed grasses. They kicked up their heels and sang to the moon in joy. An added satisfaction was Sagittarius' good manners. He always stood aside to let Altair have the first bites of hay or river grass.

One morning the two donkeys were standing by the low-slatted wall in the garden. Candace and Mary were bathing the child in a shallow dish of pottery. The sun bounced in sprays of light from the tall red lilies.

'He is perfect!' Candace said to Mary. 'Like a little god. Perhaps he is a god wandering the earth as they did in the olden days. A kind of light seems to impregnate his skin.' Mary said nothing, but she smiled. It was a mingled smile of pride and sadness.

While Candace was drying Jeshua in a thick cloth, clucking and laughing all the while, a beggar woman came around the corner of the house. She carried a shapeless bundle in her arms. Her clothes were filthy and in tatters.

'Alms! Alms!' she whined. 'Alms in the name of Ra! I've been starving for days now. Alms in the name of Hathor! Alms! Alms! I pray you!'

'Go away, you loathsome creature!' the gypsy shouted. 'I know your kind. You haunt the temples and the parks. Go away, I say. I've many friends among the temple police here close at hand. By the gods, I'll put you in a place where you'll beg for mercy!' The gypsy's face was red and swollen with anger.

The beggar woman did not move. 'By the heart of mercy, I swear I am in dire need. I'm starving, lady. Just give me something, anything, to eat.'

'Oh please, please, Candace!' Mary pleaded. 'Look at her. She *is* starving. I've bread and fish in the house. You keep the child. I'll run to get the food.'

The beggar woman sat on the grass with her bundle on her knees. She tore great chunks of bread with her teeth and crammed the fish in her mouth like some mad creature. Mary watched her. Altair and Sagittarius never saw a face so sad as Mary's.

When she had finished, the woman licked the ends of her fingers and wiped her hands on the grass. Candace, much softened, put some silver in her hand, saying, 'There, that will keep you for several days. What brought you to this state?'

'My husband had a small piece of land,' the beggar said. 'We were happy, though we sweated and worked the whole day long. Then just before my baby came, my husband had an argument with the Roman tax gatherer. They took him to the galleys.' The pinched face was contorted with anguish. 'See? I am too weak to cry. I went mad for a time, I think. I wandered through the countryside not knowing where I was. My child was born in the fields.'

'Your child?'

'Yes, he's here on my knee. That's why I begged for food. I had no milk to nurse him. He's starving, too.'

Candace was aroused. Her plump hands beat the air. 'By the gods,' she cried, 'these Romans are swine!' She gave Jeshua to Mary. 'There's a jug of milk near the fire. I'll get it, and a bowl and a soft rag. We can persuade the child to eat, I think.'

She came back in a moment and took the filthy bundle from the beggar. Pulling back the layers of cloth she came at length to a face so tiny it seemed

made for a doll. The child scarcely breathed. A cry
of pity broke from the lips of Candace. Mary gazed
upon the scene with a look that warmed the heart of
the poor mother.

Candace dipped the cloth into the milk and with it
moistened the lips of the child, then dipped it again,
gently opening the child's lips and squeezing it into
his mouth. A faint cry came forth like a kitten mew-
ing.

'I've laced the milk with wine,' Candace said. 'I
think he should come around.' Her words proved true.
After a little time the child began to suck vigorously
on the rag.

Mary had brought some clean cloths and a woven
shawl. 'The child is filthy,' she said to Candace.
'There has been no chance to keep him clean. Come,
let's bathe him in the water here. It's still tepid and,
strangely enough, it's clear as it was before we gave
Jeshua his bath.'

'That's splendid!' Candace agreed. But when she
uncovered the wasted body of the child a quick
cry escaped her. 'O Mary! No!' The child's body was
covered with scaly sores. 'No!' We dare not bathe
him here at all. He has leprosy! It would be better if
he died. We cannot even keep him here!'

'I have no fear,' Mary said.

'But Jeshua. Think of him. Think of the danger.
His beauty marred forever! Oh no!'

'I *have* thought,' Mary said. 'Men may be evil, but

God is good. I have a flask of myrrh. It was the gift of a king. Once on the way here I saw it cure a horrid sore, all in a moment. Let me get the flask and try it on the child. We can bathe him first, dry him, and then use the remedy. After all, the dish is made of clay. It's not too dear. With Joseph working now, we can afford to break the dish and burn the cloth, if it seems wise to do so.'

Candace protested with strong words, but Mary had her way. She brought the flask of myrrh and put the baby in the water, bathing him gently. Then she folded him in a soft cloth and patted it all over. The beggar woman sat and watched them, too weak to move.

When the child was dry Mary pulled back the folds of cloth. Altair was so surprised at what she saw that a little cry escaped her. The sores had disappeared from the frail body. The flesh was whole, pinkish yellow in color. Mary held him in her arms. Her eyes were wide with wonder. As for Candace, she buried her face in Jeshua's shoulder weeping. Over and over she said, 'Child! Child! Who are you?'

Candace kept the baby and his mother for several days. One morning the beggar woman said, 'I have a sister far away from here. She lives in the country. I know I could find work with her, if I could get there.'

'The child is doing well,' Candace replied. 'Surely you would not want to take him on the road.' Her voice grew wheedling. 'Leave him here awhile until you are settled in. I'll take good care of him. Meanwhile, I'll give you money for the road.'

So it was settled. The woman went away. Candace could hardly bear to leave the house, so absorbed was she in the child left with her.

'The gods are kind,' she said. 'Perhaps the woman may never return. It's true this baby is not beautiful like Jeshua. But he'll be mine, at least for a time. His eyes are beautiful and large. Soon I'll have him fat as butter. You'll see.'

'It will be a fine thing for both of you,' Mary said. 'Our God is good!'

'Yet, I have you to thank, Mary, not God. If you had not come here, this never would have happened.'

'Who knows?' Mary was smiling. 'The stars that you swear by should have told you this long ago.'

'The stars! No wonder you smile. I saw in your eyes, the day you came, that you knew the past and future meant nothing more to me than my own shrewdness.'

'You're right, Candace,' Mary assented. 'You knew from our clothes and faces just what you said. You guessed the rest.'

'It's true! Only too true. I have found it is easy to guess for gold, but the coinage of the heart is hard to find.'

'That is what I thought the day I met you,' Mary answered. 'Here's one, I said to myself, whose heart is empty like her rooms.'

Before the new spring wove its wreath of shining flowers for the land of Egypt, my mother was born to Altair. When Mary saw the little new-born foal lying on the grass one morning she called to Candace, 'Hurry out! Altair has had her child.'

'He's at once funny and charming!' Candace said, looking down over the fat shoulder of the beggar's child cuddled in the crook of her arm.

Hearing the noise, Joseph joined the group. He got down on one knee and stroked the little leggy creature. 'Notice how she shines! She has a gloss that fairly outdoes both Sagittarius and Altair. She's brighter by far than a new-coined denarius.'

That's how my mother got her name, Denarius, and became the pet of the child in those first years when he was growing in strength and wisdom. But that's another story.

Summer came to Memphis in a blaze of heat that seemed to sear the brain. A hot wind blew for months. Joseph working at his bench sweated over the three-cornered stools he made and hawked about the streets. A row of them stood always ready for sale beneath the striped awning at the front of the house.

Altair could see that Joseph yearned for the coolness of Nazareth. He never said a word, but his eyes stared off into space each time he wiped the sweat from his forehead.

Once Altair heard him say to Mary, 'The angel in my dream ordered me to stay in Egypt until I was told to return. Almost every night I think I'll see the angel again, but I never do.'

'The child is safe,' Mary said. 'That is all that matters.'

'True,' Joseph replied. 'But I realize it is hard for you to be exiled from your family and your people.'

'*He* is our people,' Mary cried. Joseph bent his head when he heard her say these words.

Mary had set up her loom in the garden near Joseph's bench. Her fingers seemed to have a mind of their own. She let them fly as they would. Her eyes were always watching Jeshua where he tumbled and played on a rug at her feet. If Candace was out on business, Mary would put the beggar's child on the rug beside her son. The two children looked at each other with solemn eyes. They were like two ripe apples hanging on a tree.

When autumn came the air grew cooler. One day all the storks went flying north in a line. That was the morning the bluebird suddenly appeared in the gypsy's garden. Mary and Candace were busy in the house. Jeshua was creeping about on his rug, fondling the silver horse he had received as a gift in Bethlehem. Altair, standing nearby, was amazed to see her old friend, the bluebird, sitting on the wall. She perched there in misery. One wing was broken and she hung her rumpled head.

'O Altair, my joy is gone forevermore!' the bluebird said.

'What's wrong?'

'This summer I had four lovely children, bluer than the sky. I taught them to catch locusts on the trees, and fat worms in the river mud, after they learned to fly. We were all going north tomorrow. But yesterday an evil boy near the river struck me with a stone. My wing is broken. I must stay behind. Per haps never again can I lose myself in the radiant atmosphere you call the air, or see my mate again.'

Altair's heart was big with sorrow to see her friend in pain. Then her eyes brightened. 'Fly down beside the child on the rug,' she said, 'if you can. Mary will soon come out, for she never tires watching her son. She has a flask of healing myrrh.'

'But how can that straighten my broken bones and knit them whole again?'

'I can't answer that question because I don't know the answer. At least your pain will cease. And that is something.'

'But who will cure the pain of my heart?'

'The coming days alone can do that. At least there's no harm in trying what I suggest.'

With painful effort the bird flopped on the grass. Nearer and nearer she dragged her crippled wing, hopping toward the rug on which the child crept after the silver horse.

At last the child noticed the bluebird. He stopped and looked at her as if her sad chirp was the only sound in the world. Then a smile broke on his baby face. Little by little he moved toward the bird until his little right hand, which he extended slowly, touched her feathers so lightly it seemed itself a feather.

The bluebird trembled all over. Suddenly she gave a loud chirp, shook out all her feathers, and jumped on the shoulder of the child. The unexpected movement made him start. He rolled over on his back, kicking his chubby feet in delight, and Altair heard his gleeful gurgle.

Then the bluebird darted up into the air. She flew and flew in circles, careening joyfully, then perched briefly to sing her song before flying away.

Sagittarius who had watched the scene with Altair said, 'I think she hadn't hurt her wing at all. Perhaps she tried to test your friendship. Women are strange —I mean lady birds are!' Sagittarius went on talking and Altair was glad he did, so he would not notice the two big tears that rolled down her nose.

With the first days of the full summer heat Joseph grew restless and yearned for Nazareth. Jeshua was walking now. He toddled about the garden, and the other child crept after him like a fat shadow. Altair took great delight in watching them. Sometimes Jeshua would catch the smaller boy by the hand until he stood erect and took a step or two.

Yet, as Candace said to Mary, 'Despite the fact that they go everywhere, the garden never looked so fine. The grass is greener, and all the flowers have many more blooms than any year since I have been here.'

'It's a good year,' Mary said. 'The spring came early.'

'There's much more to be said than that.' Candace was emphatic. 'But I'll not say all that's in my mind. Your child has a strange power over the earth and all that's in it.'

'His time has not yet come.'

'Perhaps not. One thing I'm sure of. He is no common mortal. I saw it the first day I looked at him. I was tempted to tell my clients about him after he cured my borrowed son. I could have made more gold than Croesus had.'

'I thanked you in my heart for your forbearance,' Mary said. And Candace knew that Mary had dismissed the subject.

That night Altair was wakened by footsteps softly approaching. Joseph came toward her, and in the bright moonlight she saw his face, transfigured by a smile. He patted her when he reached the wall where Altair stood with Sagittarius and Denarius.

'We'll soon be going home, little star,' he said. 'At last! At last! I saw the angel. In my first sleep he came, bright with the glory of our God. Herod is dead, he told me! Return to Nazareth! Oh, Altair, I have longed to hear those words! I'll not sleep again tonight, for my thoughts are on the morrow.

When Mary wakes, we'll pack our things and start on the long road back to Nazareth.'

Next morning Candace did her best to persuade Mary and Joseph to linger on in Memphis. But Joseph would not budge from his resolve.

'The angel said *Return*, and we must follow his command!'

'But the heat and the long journey. Think of Mary and Jeshua! And the little foal!'

'I do think of them, Candace, but God's word comes first. One thing I promise you. We'll travel slowly, in the morning and late evening. I'm sure Mary must want to see our house in Nazareth.'

'I do! Oh, I do, Joseph! It is very dear to me. After two years there will be many things to be done before it's clean and bright again.'

Candace, seeing herself defeated, wept awhile. At length she dried her tears and said to Mary, 'You and your child have brought me many things. Not only my own child—for now I am sure the beggar woman will not return—but, along with the child I longed for, you brought me knowledge of the one true God, and peace in Him.'

'I am glad you are happy, Candace.'

'I'm more than happy, grateful is the word.'

'We know that as well as we know this garden. You have been good to us these months.'

'Being good is far, far too little. Gratitude must

overflow in deeds that match the gifts received. I have a client in Alexandria. Demetrius is his name. He's master of many slaves and many caravans. I'll never forget the night he came to this house wearing the dirty dress of a Roman slave. Of course his hands were white and soft. Underneath his rumpled hair his hawk-nosed face had the imperial look of a man who gives commands and never takes one.'

Candace laughed all over, like a shaken dish of curds, as she recalled what followed. 'I found more wisdom than a sibyl, and made him think I was wiser than Plato. Each time he's up this way, he comes for new advice. It's always favorable, of course, because he's not the kind who loses to anyone. Joseph shall take a letter to him with my seal. Then you can join the caravan moving north and have the protection of his care.'

In the end Candace and her child, on Sagittarius, came down as far as Alexandria with their guests. All things were settled with Demetrius. The morning of departure came. Altair found it hard to say which wailed the louder, Candace or Sagittarius.

Mary did her best to console Candace when she said, 'We'll carry you in our hearts a whole life long. We shall all be one in prayer, forevermore.'"

Balo's story was broken at this point. A great spear of lightning tore the sky asunder.

"The rain will come from the west," Sapor said.

"Run with me to the curved wall of the temple. That offers some protection, poor as it is."

The donkeys rushed after Sapor. Then the sky opened and the rain came down like a great waterfall. The donkeys huddled together near the wall. They were cold and miserable, and joined in the unhappy cries of Balo between the rumble of the thunder.

∼ FIVE ∼

Sapor was late. He came across the corral from the south gate. He raised his long head and stared at the north gate where Balo was trotting up and down, screaming at the top of her lungs. The little foal stood some distance away; her head hung down in sadness.

Amarillis hurried to him, saying, "Sapor, you must do something. I think Balo has lost her mind. She does nothing but run from gate to gate."

"I'll soon put a stop to that," Sapor said. His yellow eyes twinkled with intelligence. "Call the other donkeys here."

Amarillis ran to execute his will. Soon she was back with Nemo, Nabal, and the others.

"Come with me," Sapor commanded. "We'll rush in and hem Balo round. Then when she's quiet once again, I'll make her tell me what is wrong with her."

The donkeys surrounded Balo. The air was filled with dust and clods of dried mud kicked up by their churning hoofs. Slowly, little by little, they pressed Balo toward the center of the corral.

"Stop! Stop it, I say!" Balo screamed at last. "You're stifling me."

"You well deserve it," Sapor cried. "Shame, and shame again! Here we have the loveliest day of spring. The almond trees are like clouds of silver butterflies and all the air is sweet. Someone has brought us fresh meadow grass. Why must you cry and carry on like a demented thing?"

"What is hay to me even if it come from Nazareth? And almond trees? Or spring? My heart is bursting with the injustice done me."

"The world is hardly ever just," Nemo said mildly. "The needle in the haystack men talk about is much more quickly found. But found in the hay is not too agreeable to all our kind."

"You speak in riddles," Balo snorted. "Now my riddle's solved. I saw him! I saw him today. Yes, this very day."

"Who speaks in riddles?" Amarillis questioned. "Are we mind readers that we can know just what you saw, or whom—unless you tell us?"

A great sob broke from Balo's throat. "It was he at last—my long-sought Jeshua. It's now almost two years since I told you of his wondrous birth in Bethlehem and all that followed. I hoped to see him here in Jerusalem but my heart was weary and my hope was dying. Today—this very day—I saw him! My own, dear, noble master! I felt his gentle hand upon my head. I beg you stand away and give me air. I'll tell you how it came about. Then you will know why

I must find some way to leave this loathsome place and go to him."

The donkeys slowly broke their ranks and Sapor said, "Great things are coming to you, Balo. I'm sure I speak for all of us when I say I'm all on tenterhooks to know just how you found him and how he looked. Come, stand away a little, Amarillis. Don't crowd and breathe so hard, until we hear the happy ending of this tale."

Then, in a somewhat breathless voice, Balo began her story.

"This morning, very early, I was tethered near an inn outside the south gate of the city. Sunrise still flushed the hills with pink that turned the olive trees to mother of pearl. The morning seemed enchanted. The air was like a gentle child's kiss. Somehow, I cannot tell you why, my heart was lighter than the thistledown. I felt a sense of happiness like I used to know in Nazareth, standing along the little river knee-deep in grass. A sense of urgency was on me too. I groomed myself as my mother taught me to at home, and then I sleeked my child until he shone like Caesar's great silver platter. What I was getting ready for I did not know, but I knew somehow that a great joy awaited me in the day ahead.

Then, looking about on the roadside, I saw that I was not the only one who seemed to be waiting for

some great thing. Though it was very early the road
was already becoming crowded like it is on the eve
of the Sabbath, when merchants with their donkeys
and camels choke the southern gate and everyone
hurries to get home before the first star of the Sabbath pierces the sky with its crystal lance. Amid the
vast throngs the people gathered in little knots.
Everyone was talking. There was such a babble of
sound that words were swallowed up in noise.

Business was brisk with us. Much talk and shouting dry the mouth and prepare the way for thirst.
Long before the sun grew hot my heavy jars were
lighter than my heart. My master's face seemed one
vast tooth. He charged them double the cupful. Then
triple. He clapped his thigh with glee each time they
paid, proud of his shrewdness and cupidity. Somehow, as I watched him, sadness flowed into my joy
like water mixed with wine.

And then I began to notice the people in the growing crowd that craned their necks backward to the
road that stretches out toward Bethany. Many were
farmers and rough fishermen. Their bronzed faces
and strong callused hands were like maps of days
spent in the sun and wind. That something unusual
was afoot showed in the pure white of their new-
washed clothes and in their shining faces. An oc-
casional Roman sauntered by in his high-lashed
sandals, looking at everyone with amused eyes, like

some wide-traveled man returning home and finding the yokelry from which he sprang. Soldiers were there, moving in and out among the crowd. Not keeping order, mind you, but free from discipline, waiting to be astonished or amused and winking at the young maids from the country towns. Matrons from the city I saw, merchants and Levites, Pharisees with their purple fringes and important stride. But all these were less numerous than the beggars and the sick. It broke my heart to see so many ill and suffering.

Under the scattered shadow of a tall palm the lepers huddled together, their chewed-up faces covered with filthy rags. A keening cry came from their lips, 'Unclean, unclean!' The other pilgrims left a frame of wide space about the lepers, scorning their shade. Even the dogs were full of fear. They went slinking along the edge of the shadow as if it were sown with dragon's teeth.

The blind were everywhere. Some of them were led by friends or relations, holding one hand to guide them. Others, alone, stumbled along on canes. The bolder spirits shook their cups crying, 'Alms in the name of God!' It seemed that the sick of the world had gathered along the grassy roadsides, carried on pallets, with their great haunted eyes brilliant with pain and fever. Cripples there were, and those possessed of devils.

But strong or sick, whoever wanted water, my master charged them all the same. I saw him strike a lame man who tried to catch in his cup a tiny trickle from one jar.

When both jars were drained to the very lees, my master gave a glad shout, tossed the last silver coin in the air, and caught it in one hand. His joy was exuberant. Then he led me near the inn and tied my halter to an olive tree. His hard hand slapped me once across the nose, and he was gone to keep his tryst with wine.

I watched the ever-growing crowd and nursed my foal. One beggar child with wide brown eyes came by. He patted my head with his satin fingers, then bent to stroke my child. That moment I longed for human speech. I wanted to ask why all those people seemed delirious with excitement.

I did hear one bearded stranger say to his smooth-faced child, 'It is the Kingdom. At last it's here. There will be bread and food for everyone. Oh, child, I saw it with my own eyes, or I would not believe it. Seven barley loaves and a few little fishes. We sat on the thick grass. I thought he must be daft to think that he could feed five thousand men with bread for ten. He broke and blessed the food and then his friends brought it to us. We ate until we were filled to the ears. If I had not seen it with my own eyes . . . It is the Kingdom, and the end of Rome for us. Hosanna! That I lived to see . . .' They passed beyond my straining ears. Oh, how I ached to know what was the meaning of it all!

Just how long I stood there in the thickening crowd, I cannot guess.

Suddenly I saw two men walking along the center of the road. The sunlight caught the white of hooded cloaks. They looked right and left as if they sought a friend, or some important person. When they were near to where I stood their eyes lit up. Nodding to each other they came through the crowd. The people must have known them for they made way without one detaining gesture.

I was amazed when both men stopped right where I stood. They had a smiling gravity like men you trust at sight, and I was not afraid. 'It's just as he said,' one told the other. 'She and her foal.' He put out his hand and untied the loose knot on my halter rope. 'Come,' he said to me gently. 'You have been chosen well; slender and gentle and shining like well-used silver coins.' He lifted my wooden yoke with its empty water jars and laid them on the grass.

I trembled at his words. It had been so long since anyone had praised me. Could it be, I asked myself, that some new master has bought us, someone who loves us and will treat us gently in the days to come?

We walked through the crowd and started down the road. Some men called out as we passed, 'Hurry and bring him to us before the noonday sun makes us faint on the way.'

Down, down the road we went. The moments seemed endless to my impatient heart. At last the crowd grew thinner. Then we stopped before a low-walled house. A group of men waited there, wearing the same hooded cloaks of glittering white from which bronzed faces shone, copper in snow. One seemed to be their leader; a red beard jutted from his chin.

'At last,' he said, 'you're here. The sun grows hot. The Master waits inside. I'll call him.'

He turned beneath the shadow of the door. 'Our cloaks will be his saddle.' Suiting his words to action, he threw back the hood, took off his cloak, and handed it to a strong young man they called Mark. The others standing by followed suit, folding their white cloaks like a soft pillow across my back.

When they were finished several women stepped forward from the low shadow of the house. One was a tall imperial-looking beauty, with crowns of russet-colored braids piled high on her head. She moved as dancers move, with the easy grace of water flowing down a hill.

'It's not enough,' she said, taking a priceless shawl of Tyrian purple from her shoulders. 'Is Magdalen so poor that use waits on magnificence? It shall not be.'

Some of the women came to help as she draped the shining silk in artful folds above the cloaks until the fringes almost swept the road. Others rushed to the edge of the fields, and the trees heavy with flowers. Sooner than words can fit to tell it, my neck was hung with plaited wreaths. It was delightful to smell their blended perfume—like dreams of all the things we donkeys love: grass and flowers and placid meadows dreaming in the sun.

Soon after this a man stood framed in the door of the house. His hair was grizzled; his face like carved cedar spoke of strength.

'All is ready?' he asked.

'Yes, ready indeed,' Mark said. 'Like the kings of old, like royal David, he shall enter David's city riding a royal beast as David did.'

A shout went up from everyone. I turned my head. There in the door a man was standing. Such a man my eyes had never seen. He towered above the others like the cedars of Lebanon. Slim, strong, wide of shoulders. His bearded head was poised like a well-set jewel, framed in the sun-bleached thickness of his hair. More perfect than a statue from ancient Greece. No language could describe him. His features, so distinct and beautiful, combined to make a unity that dazzled like sun on water. Under level brows his eyes looked out, knowing but innocent, like a child who lives with sorrow. Tenderness, compassion, strength! They were all there and much more. I could have looked a hundred years that were only a beginning of delight.

'Thank you,' he said. His voice was low but it plucked at each heartstring as if that were the only one his fingers touched. And as he spoke a smile,

more in his dark eyes than at the corners of his lips, flashed out like summer lightning and was refracted from the surrounding faces of the group. She who had given her shawl was like the pillar of an alabaster lamp lit in some king's hall of state.

He came toward me gravely and as he sat upon my back his firm hand stroked my head. A tingling crept along my spine. Suddenly my heart knew! It was Jeshua, though I had heard no name. All the things my grandmother had told me flashed through my bubbling mind. All was in that moment like the green bud of a rose suddenly opened to superb reality past all belief.

For a moment I grew faint. The sky was dark before my eyes. Then my heart strengthened in its stride. I felt that I would burst with pride. But, mind you, not the pride in self that kills and despises others. It was pride in him: a great flood of happiness to be his beast of burden on this day when skies and trees breathed out a song of joy and the whole world seemed waiting for the king of kings.

Oh! I can see by your faces that you think I exaggerate. But all those standing round, even those men of his who knew him well through the years and days, were overflowing with happiness as I was. They ran to the sides of the road in all directions. They tore sprigs from the olive trees, scarlet and purple flowers from the hedges, and butter yellow, juicy sprays of fresh, young palms. These they scattered on the road underneath my hoofs. The women, not to be outdone, took the scarves from their heads and threw them on the ground ahead of me. They danced before him.

One great, strong man, in an excess of joy, sang out, 'Hosanna! Hosanna to the son of David! Blessed is he—oh, blessed is he that comes in the name of the Lord!' The people took up the chant, and it became like the noise of many waters roaring the birth of spring. The crowd thronged all about us, but with respect. Oh, it was a strange and wondrous thing!

I could not see him sitting on my back. But I knew he sat there like a statue with that look upon his face of tranquil compassion, from which love streams out with healing.

Strangest of all, the lame and the blind, even the lepers, seemed to forget their pain. They too took up the chant, 'Hosanna! Blessed is he, blessed is he . . .' And no one tried to touch him or stay his course. To praise his name, to do him honor, was their sole intent. Then, falling in behind us, they packed the whole road back to Bethany. It was as though the forest walked with the waving palms they held. The trees seemed to ring, and the very stones cried out the echoing voices.

At the city gate no man came forward, as they usually do to say a word or ask us whence we came or where we went. The Roman soldiers stood like men of bronze, eyes opened wide. Some of them, caught in the delirium of joy, shouted 'Hosanna!' with the crowd.

Then we were in the narrow streets with the jutting walls. From the balconies overhead women leaned down. My feet on the stones were muffled in a rain of scarves and shawls, silken handkerchiefs, and flowers, like a royal carpet spread in the great hall of a king. One woman caught a ruby from her hair and threw it down. Others poured precious flasks of perfume on the stones.

From one end of the twisting road a cripple staggered out of the crowd. He was bent on his crutch, like the pins women use to hold their hair in place. The shadow of Jeshua fell on him. And in a twinkling he straightened his body and threw away his crutch. A look of glad amazement, that pierced him like a sword, flashed on his face. Tears rained down, he fell on his knees. 'Hosanna! Hosanna!' he cried over and over, like one broken on the rack of joy.

His cure turned the delight of the crowd to complete delirium. They surged forward. A thousand hands reached up like leaves blown by the autumn wind.

Jeshua never moved, except to place his hand between my ears in reassurance. My child huddled beneath me, terrified at first, then stood there like a stone until the way was cleared for us to go up the steep incline to the temple, shining with gold and scarlet in the blazing sun.

At last we came to the gate called Beautiful. It towered above us. The carved vines and flowers, running riot upon it, danced in the light and seemed alive.

Jeshua's friends gathered around him when he dismounted from my back. They took their hooded cloaks and draped them on their arms. The beautiful woman who had followed close beside us gathered her shawl to her breast as if it were now doubly precious.

My Master's hand was laid in warm thanks on my nose. Then, followed by the crowd, he entered the gate. The hosannas reached a peak of acclaim that grew faint and fainter, as the massive walls swallowed the ringing sound.

The square was so silent I could hear the beetles crawling on the stones. Slowly, like a child with a honey cake savoring each slow bite, I savored my memories of Jeshua. Doubtless he would return. My days would be spent in glory at his side, sharing the glory of the king that he was meant to be. Master of masters, how good. . . .

I heard the grating voice of the Gypsy: 'Well, there you are, pig-headed one!'

My dreams crashed down like an alabaster pane struck with a blacksmith's hammer.

'Back you go to your pen. You lazy beast!' he shouted.

I set my foot and jaws. He pulled and dragged me. He took his whip and lashed me until I screamed with pain. He also struck my colt, again and again. It was then my heart turned to water. Slowly, we came here. Now you know why I must find some way to break the gate. My heart is not here. It waits before the gate called Beautiful."

Balo filled the air with mournful cries. The others stood about her in a ring. Their eyes were empty and they stared on emptiness.

SIX

THE DONKEYS were pressed together in the middle of the corral. Their eyes held a frightened look and they constantly cast uneasy glances over their shoulders. Sapor, at last, lifted his head above them. "It's been several hours now since the earth has stopped its trembling."

"But will it come again?" Amarillis questioned.

"Who knows?" Sapor replied. "At least here in the open we are safe. Unless a crack should open in the earth. That's why I ordered you to come away from the wall of the theater. It might tumble down and end us all."

The donkeys stirred uneasily. Amarillis cried a little in a soft voice.

"Oh, Sapor, I'm frightened," she said. "I'm really frightened. It was such a lovely day. My master tied me in a little park near Herod's palace. There was a light breeze in the air. I nibbled wisps of grass, dreaming of happy days. Suddenly the trees stopped their singing. The air grew deathly still. The leaves trembled with some foreknowledge. My feet seemed stuck to the stones. I was too frightened to shudder even. I felt myself carved in snow, ice was in my blood and heart—my very bones. Then my eyes glanced upward toward the unscarred blue.

"A green-black cloud, that looked like a gigantic hand, came from the horizon to the east. Slowly its fingers lengthened, like tremendous snakes launching themselves across the floor of heaven. They writhed and turned, erasing the blue with menacing green. It seemed to fall in flakes until the air about me was green as bile. I choked as I breathed it. Little by little, the green turned dark, then blacker than night in some far cave where lost men tear their throats at the impenetrable darkness pressing in from every side. A great sword of lightning split the clouds, followed by another and another, until the sky seemed one vast blaze of sickening blue. The air smelled of death and evil that invaded the deep caverns of the brain. Then the thunder roared and crackled, louder than I have ever heard it. The hills cried aloud with furious echoes.

"At length the earth shuddered. It seemed in the throes of agony. I fell on my knees, straining at my rope, while the shudder made the stones crack with noise like a great catapult when the spring snaps in the midst of battle. It was then I saw them running through the streets. Oh, no, no! They weren't people as we know them, but shades darker than the air about me. They cried aloud; cried and wailed again. The grave cloths wound about them fluttered with the speed of their flight. Their voices pierced the thunder. What they were crying I could not understand. But it was a noise of sorrow and lamentation, pounding at the very gates of the sky.

"As suddenly as it began, the earth stopped its motion. The darkness stayed. I rose to my feet expecting another shock each moment. So I stood until my master came. His face was pale as ashes. 'Oh!' he cried, over and over. He did not mount me, but he led me here swiftly, crying out, 'Oh! Oh!' over and over, wordless with some piercing sorrow."

"They say that the plates and wine jugs danced in all the houses like drunken things," Nabal said. "I heard that Herod cried like a child under a lashing, lying flat upon his silken bed. He sprinkled his greasy curls with ashes. People ran from their homes. They prayed in the streets, lifting their hands in terror."

"Not even the house of God was spared, so I heard," Sapor added breathlessly. "The towering pillars swayed, cracks ran along the massive walls anchored in solid mother rock. Water slopped out of the brazen lavers. The fires were quenched in the pits of sacrifice. The air was salted with blood. While the attending priest gaped in terror, the gold and rainbow veil that shields the holy of the holies from all prying eyes was torn from top to bottom as if Goliath's hand had reached from hell to rend its seamless fabric."

The donkeys were so interested in recounting their

tale of terror that they did not see Balo and her foal approaching from the southern gate. Finally they heard her voice crying with the pathos of a forsaken child. With one accord they turned to look. Balo's head drooped down almost to her hoofs. She stumbled along as if she were blind.

Sapor ran toward her. Nemo and Amarillis followed close on his heels.

"Balo!" Sapor cried in his deep voice. "Are you hurt?"

"Don't be frightened," Amarillis said. "The worst of the shock seems over."

"Courage, Balo!" Nemo chimed in. "Courage! The earthquake is over now. Be brave and do not fear."

By slow degrees Balo raised her head. Sapor could see her eyes were flecked with blood.

"Earthquake?" she said. "What earthquake?"

Sapor and the other donkeys looked at her in amazement. "You didn't feel the earthquake?" they shouted.

"No," Balo answered, "I felt no earthquake." She gave a piercing cry that stilled the gabbling voices. When she spoke it was almost in a whisper. "My heart is dead. It died with him today. If all the earth fell down and floated away in smoke I should not care. My brain is burning with the things I saw this day. Now I know there is nothing, nothing but grief and evil forevermore."

"Where were you, Balo," Sapor asked, "that you escaped the earthquake?"

"Where was I?" Balo echoed. "I hardly know. This day has been a thousand years long since early morn till now. My wits are all confused."

Her voice broke, then strengthened a little as she went on:

"It started this morning early, as we made the last of our rounds near the edge of the city. Some friend of the Gypsy's saw him and ran up to tell him something. What it was I do not know. But in a moment they were both babbling away in their own tongue. At last my master clapped his hands. There was a look on his face such as a wolf has when he has torn the throat of a lamb and laps his blood.

'Oh, splendid, splendid!' he said at last. 'This I must see.' He rubbed his hands together. 'I'll meet you in the court before Pilate's judgment seat. The water's nearly gone. I won't be long.'

What it was he was so eager to see I tried to guess. I racked my brains. It was getting near the great Sabbath. Perhaps some queen was coming to visit Pilate, hoping to be amused by the strange antics of the Jews. Perhaps a new Roman governor had been appointed. Whatever it was, it picked at the Gypsy's mind like a burr caught in a woolen robe. He hurried me through the crooked streets bawling and shouting, 'Water,' like a crazy man. In one of the pauses we heard the dim echo of men's voices raised in anger. It was ever so faint, barely detectable. But it made the Gypsy so excited that he had had enough of water selling.

His hands were shaking as he tied my halter rope about a post near the edge of a vacant place overgrown with weeds. 'There's not much water left,' he muttered to himself. 'I'll sell it later when the sun gets fierce above the city.' Quickly he lifted the straps holding the water jars. He lifted them off with a curse and hid them in the midst of the thick-grown weeds. Then he ran off down the street. His sandals made a clopping noise. My foal and I were left to our own thoughts and peace.

My thoughts were all of Jeshua. Somehow I felt he recognized me that last Sabbath when he rode upon my back. Why should I have been selected, if it were not true? His hand on my head, the reassuring caress along my nose outside the Beautiful Gate, these were signs of his love, I felt sure. But why had he not looked for me? Since he had known where to find me for his triumph, surely he knew where I was now. My mind went round and round like one of our kind tied to the shaft of a mill for grinding corn.

How beautiful he was! How kingly and kind; kind beyond all men who walked the earth. Still I could not understand it. Such a kindly man must know how terribly I suffered. Surely he would seek me out and take me from the Gypsy, by force if necessary. After all, I had been stolen as a child. That injustice was multiplied, compounded as it were, in days of sun and cold. Days without food. Beatings and curses. The dice were loaded against me, and my heart cried out against the injustice. Last of all, the Gypsy had struck my child. What could my foal's future be but lashes and eternal slavery?

We stood there all morning while I turned such thoughts over as a haymaker with his fork turns the grass of the field until it is cured. My rope was short. I could barely reach the top of the weeds that matted the vacant place. They were green and fresh with winter rain, and gave consolation to my tongue at least and sure relief from thirst.

In time, as I nibbled, I noticed all the weeds were covered with tiny blue stars so delicate the eye could scarcely see them. My mind went rushing back to Altair's story about the great star that shone in the sky when Jeshua was born. 'King of Kings,' the wise men called him. I could not doubt it after the last triumphant Sabbath.

Once again I heard the distant echo of many voices. It came fairly strong on the wings of the warm breeze. It made my heart uneasy, for I detected in it a note of rage such as one hears when many men are crazed with anger. Fear gnawed at my heart like a mouse gnawing at a cupboard door, making way to enter.

It was then I first noticed my rope and how poorly

it was tied. Usually the Gypsy ties a knot that baffles me. Often he's bragged about it to my very face.

'Untie that, you ugly beast,' he brags. Then laughing his nasty laugh he leaves me.

Oh, I tried many times to untie his knots when my heart was hot with rage and loathing. Each time I tried I failed in the attempt. The rope itself, of woven horsehair, was far too strong to break.

But this morning in his haste, or because his mind was elsewhere, the Gypsy had tied my rope with two ordinary knots. They were strongly tied, but I laughed in my heart to think how easy it would be to loose myself. It's well said, I thought, that God helps those who help themselves. The important thing was, did I have time to do it?

I started to work. My heart was bursting with impatience. I had waited, it seemed forever, for this day. My mind ran on ahead of my busy teeth. Once I was free, my foal and I would take the road to Bethany, and then to Nazareth. We would avoid the main roads and travel by night. Every man would be our enemy until we were safe in Nazareth. That old scar on my knee—Mary and Joseph could not fail to know me.

At last the second knot came free. The rope uncoiled from the post. I looked down the street. It was deserted. In my throat a great cry bubbled. My child looked up at me in wide-eyed terror. 'Come,' I said, 'my dear one. We are free forevermore!'

We trotted down the street. I knew the town by heart. Soon we were on the road to Bethany. As we trotted along blithely I began to feel uneasy once again. No Roman soldiers were standing at the city gate. Never before had I seen it left unguarded. The streets were all deserted; not even a dog went slinking along the wall. The silence terrified me more than noise would. What did it mean? Some portent of evil, I was sure of that.

The road to Bethany was still as death. We trotted on until we reached the house where Jeshua had been on the last Sabbath day. There was no sign of life about it anywhere. I looked over the wall. The silence there was worse than thunder.

My child was tired. I had to let him rest a little while. After he fed I noticed how he trembled. I touched his nose but it was warm, so I knew that he was well.

When we took to the road again I was still determined to go to Nazareth. But something drew my mind and feet back to the city. I *had* to go there. Perhaps, I reasoned to myself, Jeshua is being crowned king today—the king his joyous welcome to the city promised. Perhaps that's why my feet are drawn to go this way. The thought brought me such powerful reassurance that my heart forgot to fear. It must be that. It had to be.

Just before the city gate I paused in fear. It was still deserted, but in spite of the power drawing me

I hesitated to go inside the walls. The Gypsy, if he were already looking for me, could easily pen me up and catch me. Followed by my child, I skirted the fields and valleys along the south wall. We came at length to the deeper valley where they burn the refuse from the city. A pall of acrid smoke hung over it. My foal halted in fear. I urged him on through the burning piles that have given their name to hell. Faint smoke followed us like wraiths of hounds on the scent.

Then I saw a crowd. I think all of Jerusalem was there, toiling up the rocky slope: visitors, Romans, Jews, from the ends of the earth. And in their midst, ringed by soldiers, a bloodstained figure that half-crawled over the stony ground. Stumbled erect, then fell and crawled again, slowly, slowly, like a wounded fawn whose life-blood drips on the thorns and brambles as he is pursued by the hunter.

Evil I hate. I felt it here like an iron hand squeezing my heart. But I could not run away. Timidly I followed at the edge of the crowd, to the top of the hill. A man with bulging muscles stood there in the harsh light. He had thrown the beams of a heavy cross on the sparse grass. The rough soldiers urged the bloodstained figure forward. They took his robe off with obscene jokes, then tore his undergarment away revealing a body crisscrossed with the bloody welts from the bone-tipped scourges they had used. The figure turned around toward me. In my blurred eyes it seemed that he was clothed in a robe of glittering scarlet more glowing than the robe of state that Caesar wears. A crown was on his bleeding head, long spiky thorns. But he wore it with a regal majesty.

It could not be! Oh, it could not be! My heart cried out, remembering the way strewn with bright flowers and the voices singing 'Hosanna.' Yet I knew, at that moment, who it was. My master—Jeshua! A sword went through my heart. What did it mean? How had it come about?

Meek as a lamb he knelt and then stretched himself painfully on the cross. A soldier caught his right hand; he stretched it out. A massive hammer flashed in the sun. In five quick thudding strokes a huge spike held my master's arm to the wood, through the strong bones of the wrist. A red spurt gushed up.

The left hand next was nailed, and then both feet, against the supporting shelf that helps to make the anguish linger. Some heavy cords were wound around the body for the same cruel purpose. The harsh rope sank into the bleeding tissues like snakes burowing into spongy ground.

The soldiers slid the cross over the stones and grass to the hole prepared for it. Little by little, the soldiers swearing and grunting at the load, the cross was raised. It fell into the slot of earth with a sickening thud that jolted the bloody figure in every bone and muscle. He gave no cry, nor made a sound.

The shelf on which his feet rested almost touched the ground. Blood dripped along his legs and feet until the shelf itself was like a scarlet cushion, fringed with bloody drops.

A mocking sign in Roman script was nailed to the top of the cross on a thick piece of parchment: 'Jesus of Nazareth, King of the Jews.' This drove the crowd to fury. 'Vah! Vah! Vah!' they screamed, clenching their fists to the heavens with fiendish delight.

The Roman soldiers stood back, nodding their heads as if to say well done. They tamped the earth around the base of the cross and made an inspection of the two other crosses placed one on either side of Jeshua's. They wiped their fingers on the robes of the condemned men and stepped back, with their hairy hands upon their swords, marking a space about the crosses, beyond which no one dared to venture.

Along the edge of this narrow space the zealots danced, screaming and shouting with the noise and grunts of beasts. Many of them rasped in their throats and spat on the legs and feet that had ever been directed in paths of mercy.

One wolf-faced man called out, 'You who said you would destroy the temple and in three days raise it up again, destroy it now! Destroy it, if you can! Why don't you come down? Come down from the cross!'

The crowd took up the chant. 'Come down from the cross,' they chanted in derision. 'Come down from the cross and we'll believe.' Overcome by their own wit they flew into a frenzy of cries and cat-calls. Some threw clods of earth at the figure there. Others threw pebbles and shafts of weeds they plucked from the grass, howling with joy when an obvious hit was made.

A cry came from the cross. It was not a groan, but like the cry a deaf mute makes trying to break the barriers to speech. A haunted silence fell. Then the voice of Jeshua came, bell clear.

'Father, forgive them, they know not what they do.'

I saw him try to open his eyes. The hard dried blood hung on his lashes in great drops.

At one side of the cross a group of women stood by themselves in an anguished knot. One of them was the queenly woman who had given her purple shawl to ornament my saddle. Today all her queenliness was gone. Her shoulders drooped, her hair hung in matted disarray; tears had smudged her face like storms that buffet some beautiful temple standing on a promontory until nothing remains but a sodden ruin. Her hands were clasped on her breast in agony. With two other women there was a third who could barely stand. I knew it must be Mary, his mother. Each time she looked up at the figure on the cross her body quivered as if swords were being thrust into her heart.

Nearby was a fair young man. His hands were clasped together so tight that they seemed bloodless.

A gray-whiteness showed beneath his tanned skin. All the strong lines of his face melted into the clenched muscles standing out at the back of the jaw. From deep sockets his eyes stared out like a sleep-walker's, looking on the interior horror of nightmare dreams.

High above the din of many voices shouting their taunts I heard the cursing of the man who hung on the cross at the left of Jeshua. A contorted body and face black with rage. 'Carrion crow! Beast!' I heard him cry. And blasphemies too horrible to tell. 'Had it not been for you we might have been released. Jehovah blast you for your meddling, that brought us here to make a Roman spectacle.'

The other figure at the right of Jeshua stirred at these words. Great muscles bulged in his neck. 'For shame!' he said, in a deep halting voice. 'Oh, shame beyond the pain of dying! I know you well. Your hands are stained with blood and violence. We are guilty, but this one is innocent. O fool of Satan, this reward we merit. He is just and kind. O Lord, Lord, remember . . . remember me . . . when you have reached your kingdom.'

Jeshua's thorn-crowned head slowly came erect. That haunting voice, muffled with pain, spoke words the crowd leaned out to hear, cupping their hands to their ears.

'This day you shall be with me in Paradise.'

There was conviction in the words. I noted its effect on many of the people. Tormented expressions became grave in a moment. Some of them began to weep. Holding their hands to their faces, they turned by ones and twos and went down the hill toward the city gate, as if they could not bear to stand there any longer.

I think the crowd was getting uneasy. They were all eyes and would have watched in silence, but a word from the high priest brought a swarm of debased inciters. Shouting and cursing, they ran up and down until the people were whipped to fury. Once again the air was filled with clods and pebbles. The captain of the guard drew out his sword and gestured with displeasure at this display.

I could see that he was deeply moved. The lines of his weather-worn face deepened. They were like ruts in a muddy road left by many heavy wagons. He turned his back on the crowd, in silent contempt, squared his shoulders with a sudden shrug, and looked off toward the sun-gilded city. The knuckles of his right hand showed white. His menacing fingers touched the long hilt of his sword.

The other soldiers sat in a hollow square. Some squatted on their knees; others leaned on their elbows or sprawled at ease on the sand and grass. One red-faced guard brought out a pair of dice, while another as dark as an Ethiop threw in a heap of clothes the three victims had worn to execution. 'Here's drinking money,' he said with a laugh, then mimed a tilted bottle gurgling down his throat.

The crowd roared at his antics. They squeezed forward toward the squatting soldiers, as near as they dared. Each cast of the dice gave rise to shouted advice. The pile of clothing melted.

One last robe remained. The dark soldier held it up for everyone to see: a perfect piece of weaving stained with the blood of Jeshua. Each soldier was eager to win it. They cast the dice slowly, rolling them in their callused hands, breathed or spat on them, brandished the cubes above their head.

At this point the captain turned and sauntered over. When the last soldier had cast the dice the captain said a few sharp words I could not hear. The soldiers turned to him; their faces were like the threatening clouds rolling across the sky above them. One soldier gave him the dice. Holding his arm straight out, the captain opened his fingers and dropped the cubes in the center of his men without one gesture to the god of chance.

The red-faced soldier beat his hand against his thigh and cursed like a stream of molten lava. The dark one handed up the cloak to the captain. He took it, folded it once or twice across his arm, smoothed its folds with careful fingers, then turned his back on the scene.

Once again the figure of Jeshua stirred slowly,

slowly, to intense awareness. His glazing eyes were bent toward his mother and the fair-haired young man who stood near her. Over the roar of the crowd and the groans of the thieves crucified with him his voice rang. 'Son, this is your mother.' His gasped breath strained at the muscles of his chest. 'Mother, this is your son.' The young man heard the words, as though roused from anguished thought. Then his right arm went around Mary's shoulder. He drew her close until her weeping face found comfort there.

Perhaps he will say one word to me, I prayed in my heart. One word I can treasure like some ripe apple of sweet smell and endless savor. Cautiously I edged my way through the crowd. No one paid the least attention to me. Their eyes were fixed like tigers devouring the tortured figure of my master. So close I got to the front rank that I could feel across my shoulders the long cool shadow thrown by the cross on which he hung. I was about to lift my head when a cry broke from his bruised lips.

'My God . . . My God . . . Why have you forsaken me?'

The loneliness of the world since time began was in his voice—the loneliness of forsaken children, of men and women caught in their own traps of chance or evil—the loneliness of the vast deep before God made the light.

Many in the crowd were touched by the words. Arguments broke out. Clenched fists were shaken beneath furious eyes or sunk into living bone and flesh. 'God will come to rescue him,' some cried. 'Moses perhaps, or Elias in a fiery chariot flashing out of the sky.' The priests and Levites cried these hopes to scorn. The air was full of sounds: 'Raca! Blasphemer! Idiot!'

I noted my master's head was drooping lower. The thorns of his crown were tilted out. His beard, wet with trickling blood, spread out along his chest.

The voice of the crowd was hushed. A deepening silence fell. The captain of the guard turned round. There were tears in his eyes and his jaw was thrust out like a sword.

'I thirst,' my master called.

The captain sprang into action. Plucking one of the tall reeds growing in the grass, he dipped a sponge in myrrh and vinegar, fastened it to the end of the reed, and reached it up to the parched blue of the thirsting mouth. The blue lips grimaced. A tremendous shudder passed through the body of my master.

'It is consummated,' he cried in a voice that shook the hills and broke my heart.

Tears rolled along the thin fur of my jaw. I saw his head fall slack and then his arms and legs, in death's eternal quiet. 'It is over,' my mind babbled. 'I shall see him no more.' My front feet failed. I couldn't see. Then everything blotted out.

How long it was I do not know. First thing I knew

was the rough tongue of my child licking my face.

When I looked up I saw, under the black pall of sky, a Roman soldier with a long spear. He drove it through the breast into my master's gentle heart.

I gave one piercing cry. 'Devils from hell!' I screamed, and then I ran down the accursed hill. My foal came racing after me. I will go back to my own kind, I thought. The hearts of beasts have pity. Men have none . . . So here I am."

Balo raised her head, crying aloud to the sky, yellow with the last glow of the dying sun. Then her head dropped down. The donkeys stood in a ring of horror watching her.

Nemo spoke at last. "Balo! What's that upon your back?"

"On my back? Why, nothing. You must be mad!"

Sapor stepped forward. "No, Balo. You are wrong and Nemo's right. There is something there. Yes, it is —it is a *cross*. A cross as clear as anything." The other donkeys crowded close to see this wonder.

The words made Balo tremble. Two big tears fell from her staring eyes.

And from that night, they all remembered, the little donkey never complained again.

THE END

Nihil Obstat: REVEREND WILLIAM BUSCH
Censor Librorum
Imprimatur: JOHN GREGORY MURRAY
Archbishop of St. Paul

St. Paul, August 3, 1956

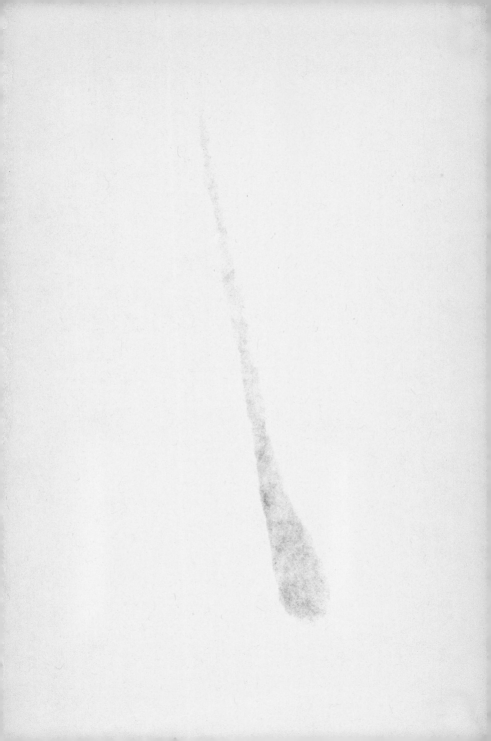